FREE Study Skills Videos/DVD Offer

Dear Customer,

Thank you for your purchase from Mometrix! We consider it an honor and a privilege that you have purchased our product and we want to ensure your satisfaction.

As part of our ongoing effort to meet the needs of test takers, we have developed a set of Study Skills Videos that we would like to give you for FREE. These videos cover our *best practices* for getting ready for your exam, from how to use our study materials to how to best prepare for the day of the test.

All that we ask is that you email us with feedback that would describe your experience so far with our product. Good, bad, or indifferent, we want to know what you think!

To get your FREE Study Skills Videos, you can use the **QR code** below, or send us an **email** at studyvideos@mometrix.com with *FREE VIDEOS* in the subject line and the following information in the body of the email:

- The name of the product you purchased.
- Your product rating on a scale of 1-5, with 5 being the highest rating.
- Your feedback. It can be long, short, or anything in between. We just want to know your impressions and experience so far with our product. (Good feedback might include how our study material met your needs and ways we might be able to make it even better. You could highlight features that you found helpful or features that you think we should add.)

If you have any questions or concerns, please don't hesitate to contact me directly.

Thanks again!

Sincerely,

Jay Willis
Vice President
jay.willis@mometrix.com
1-800-673-8175

SCAN HERE

Mometrix
TEST PREPARATION

Mometrix
TEST PREPARATION

Radiography

Prep Secrets Study Guide

Examination Review Book and Practice Test Questions

2nd Edition

Written and edited by Mometrix Test Prep

Printed in the United States of America

This paper meets the requirements of ANSI/NISO Z39.48-1992 (Permanence of Paper).

Paperback
ISBN 13: 978-1-5167-2351-5
ISBN 10: 1-5167-2351-1

Dear Future Exam Success Story

First of all, **THANK YOU** for purchasing Mometrix study materials!

Second, congratulations! You are one of the few determined test-takers who are committed to doing whatever it takes to excel on your exam. **You have come to the right place.** We developed these study materials with one goal in mind: to deliver you the information you need in a format that's concise and easy to use.

In addition to optimizing your guide for the content of the test, we've outlined our recommended steps for breaking down the preparation process into small, attainable goals so you can make sure you stay on track.

We've also analyzed the entire test-taking process, identifying the most common pitfalls and showing how you can overcome them and be ready for any curveball the test throws you.

Standardized testing is one of the biggest obstacles on your road to success, which only increases the importance of doing well in the high-pressure, high-stakes environment of test day. Your results on this test could have a significant impact on your future, and this guide provides the information and practical advice to help you achieve your full potential on test day.

Your success is our success

We would love to hear from you! If you would like to share the story of your exam success or if you have any questions or comments in regard to our products, please contact us at **800-673-8175** or **support@mometrix.com**.

Thanks again for your business and we wish you continued success!

Sincerely,
The Mometrix Test Preparation Team

Need more help? Check out our flashcards at:
http://MometrixFlashcards.com/Radiography

Written and edited by the Mometrix Exam Secrets Test Prep Team
Printed in the United States of America

TABLE OF CONTENTS

INTRODUCTION 1

SECRET KEY #1 – PLAN BIG, STUDY SMALL 2

SECRET KEY #2 – MAKE YOUR STUDYING COUNT 3

SECRET KEY #3 – PRACTICE THE RIGHT WAY 4

SECRET KEY #4 – PACE YOURSELF 6

SECRET KEY #5 – HAVE A PLAN FOR GUESSING 7

TEST-TAKING STRATEGIES 10

EXAM CONTENT/REGISTRATION 15

PATIENT CARE 16

- ETHICAL AND LEGAL ASPECTS 16
- INTERPERSONAL COMMUNICATION 26
- PHYSICAL ASSISTANCE AND MONITORING 34
- MEDICAL EMERGENCIES 39
- INFECTION CONTROL 42
- HANDLING AND DISPOSAL OF TOXIC OR HAZARDOUS MATERIAL 49
- PHARMACOLOGY 50

SAFETY 60

- PRINCIPLES OF RADIATION PHYSICS 60
- BIOLOGICAL ASPECTS OF RADIATION 67
- MINIMIZING PATIENT EXPOSURE 74
- PERSONNEL PROTECTION (ALARA) 78

IMAGE PRODUCTION 81

- IMAGE ACQUISITION AND TECHNICAL EVALUATION 81
- EQUIPMENT OPERATION AND QUALITY ASSURANCE 91

PROCEDURES 103

- HEAD, SPINE, AND PELVIS PROCEDURES 103
- THORAX AND ABDOMEN PROCEDURES 110
- EXTREMITY PROCEDURES 118

SPECIAL REPORT – DIFFICULT PATIENTS 129

SPECIAL REPORT – GUIDELINES FOR UNIVERSAL PRECAUTIONS 130

SPECIAL REPORT – BASIC REVIEW OF TYPES OF FRACTURES 131

CPR GUIDELINES FOR PROFESSIONAL RESCUERS 132

RADIOGRAPHY PRACTICE TEST 133

ANSWER KEY AND EXPLANATIONS 142

HOW TO OVERCOME TEST ANXIETY 152

ADDITIONAL BONUS MATERIAL ________ 158

Introduction

Thank you for purchasing this resource! You have made the choice to prepare yourself for a test that could have a huge impact on your future, and this guide is designed to help you be fully ready for test day. Obviously, it's important to have a solid understanding of the test material, but you also need to be prepared for the unique environment and stressors of the test, so that you can perform to the best of your abilities.

For this purpose, the first section that appears in this guide is the **Secret Keys**. We've devoted countless hours to meticulously researching what works and what doesn't, and we've boiled down our findings to the five most impactful steps you can take to improve your performance on the test. We start at the beginning with study planning and move through the preparation process, all the way to the testing strategies that will help you get the most out of what you know when you're finally sitting in front of the test.

We recommend that you start preparing for your test as far in advance as possible. However, if you've bought this guide as a last-minute study resource and only have a few days before your test, we recommend that you skip over the first two Secret Keys since they address a long-term study plan.

If you struggle with **test anxiety**, we strongly encourage you to check out our recommendations for how you can overcome it. Test anxiety is a formidable foe, but it can be beaten, and we want to make sure you have the tools you need to defeat it.

Secret Key #1 – Plan Big, Study Small

There's a lot riding on your performance. If you want to ace this test, you're going to need to keep your skills sharp and the material fresh in your mind. You need a plan that lets you review everything you need to know while still fitting in your schedule. We'll break this strategy down into three categories.

Information Organization

Start with the information you already have: the official test outline. From this, you can make a complete list of all the concepts you need to cover before the test. Organize these concepts into groups that can be studied together, and create a list of any related vocabulary you need to learn so you can brush up on any difficult terms. You'll want to keep this vocabulary list handy once you actually start studying since you may need to add to it along the way.

Time Management

Once you have your set of study concepts, decide how to spread them out over the time you have left before the test. Break your study plan into small, clear goals so you have a manageable task for each day and know exactly what you're doing. Then just focus on one small step at a time. When you manage your time this way, you don't need to spend hours at a time studying. Studying a small block of content for a short period each day helps you retain information better and avoid stressing over how much you have left to do. You can relax knowing that you have a plan to cover everything in time. In order for this strategy to be effective though, you have to start studying early and stick to your schedule. Avoid the exhaustion and futility that comes from last-minute cramming!

Study Environment

The environment you study in has a big impact on your learning. Studying in a coffee shop, while probably more enjoyable, is not likely to be as fruitful as studying in a quiet room. It's important to keep distractions to a minimum. You're only planning to study for a short block of time, so make the most of it. Don't pause to check your phone or get up to find a snack. It's also important to **avoid multitasking**. Research has consistently shown that multitasking will make your studying dramatically less effective. Your study area should also be comfortable and well-lit so you don't have the distraction of straining your eyes or sitting on an uncomfortable chair.

The time of day you study is also important. You want to be rested and alert. Don't wait until just before bedtime. Study when you'll be most likely to comprehend and remember. Even better, if you know what time of day your test will be, set that time aside for study. That way your brain will be used to working on that subject at that specific time and you'll have a better chance of recalling information.

Finally, it can be helpful to team up with others who are studying for the same test. Your actual studying should be done in as isolated an environment as possible, but the work of organizing the information and setting up the study plan can be divided up. In between study sessions, you can discuss with your teammates the concepts that you're all studying and quiz each other on the details. Just be sure that your teammates are as serious about the test as you are. If you find that your study time is being replaced with social time, you might need to find a new team.

Secret Key #2 – Make Your Studying Count

You're devoting a lot of time and effort to preparing for this test, so you want to be absolutely certain it will pay off. This means doing more than just reading the content and hoping you can remember it on test day. It's important to make every minute of study count. There are two main areas you can focus on to make your studying count.

Retention

It doesn't matter how much time you study if you can't remember the material. You need to make sure you are retaining the concepts. To check your retention of the information you're learning, try recalling it at later times with minimal prompting. Try carrying around flashcards and glance at one or two from time to time or ask a friend who's also studying for the test to quiz you.

To enhance your retention, look for ways to put the information into practice so that you can apply it rather than simply recalling it. If you're using the information in practical ways, it will be much easier to remember. Similarly, it helps to solidify a concept in your mind if you're not only reading it to yourself but also explaining it to someone else. Ask a friend to let you teach them about a concept you're a little shaky on (or speak aloud to an imaginary audience if necessary). As you try to summarize, define, give examples, and answer your friend's questions, you'll understand the concepts better and they will stay with you longer. Finally, step back for a big picture view and ask yourself how each piece of information fits with the whole subject. When you link the different concepts together and see them working together as a whole, it's easier to remember the individual components.

Finally, practice showing your work on any multi-step problems, even if you're just studying. Writing out each step you take to solve a problem will help solidify the process in your mind, and you'll be more likely to remember it during the test.

Modality

Modality simply refers to the means or method by which you study. Choosing a study modality that fits your own individual learning style is crucial. No two people learn best in exactly the same way, so it's important to know your strengths and use them to your advantage.

For example, if you learn best by visualization, focus on visualizing a concept in your mind and draw an image or a diagram. Try color-coding your notes, illustrating them, or creating symbols that will trigger your mind to recall a learned concept. If you learn best by hearing or discussing information, find a study partner who learns the same way or read aloud to yourself. Think about how to put the information in your own words. Imagine that you are giving a lecture on the topic and record yourself so you can listen to it later.

For any learning style, flashcards can be helpful. Organize the information so you can take advantage of spare moments to review. Underline key words or phrases. Use different colors for different categories. Mnemonic devices (such as creating a short list in which every item starts with the same letter) can also help with retention. Find what works best for you and use it to store the information in your mind most effectively and easily.

Secret Key #3 – Practice the Right Way

Your success on test day depends not only on how many hours you put into preparing, but also on whether you prepared the right way. It's good to check along the way to see if your studying is paying off. One of the most effective ways to do this is by taking practice tests to evaluate your progress. Practice tests are useful because they show exactly where you need to improve. Every time you take a practice test, pay special attention to these three groups of questions:

- The questions you got wrong
- The questions you had to guess on, even if you guessed right
- The questions you found difficult or slow to work through

This will show you exactly what your weak areas are, and where you need to devote more study time. Ask yourself why each of these questions gave you trouble. Was it because you didn't understand the material? Was it because you didn't remember the vocabulary? Do you need more repetitions on this type of question to build speed and confidence? Dig into those questions and figure out how you can strengthen your weak areas as you go back to review the material.

Additionally, many practice tests have a section explaining the answer choices. It can be tempting to read the explanation and think that you now have a good understanding of the concept. However, an explanation likely only covers part of the question's broader context. Even if the explanation makes perfect sense, **go back and investigate** every concept related to the question until you're positive you have a thorough understanding.

As you go along, keep in mind that the practice test is just that: practice. Memorizing these questions and answers will not be very helpful on the actual test because it is unlikely to have any of the same exact questions. If you only know the right answers to the sample questions, you won't be prepared for the real thing. **Study the concepts** until you understand them fully, and then you'll be able to answer any question that shows up on the test.

It's important to wait on the practice tests until you're ready. If you take a test on your first day of study, you may be overwhelmed by the amount of material covered and how much you need to learn. Work up to it gradually.

On test day, you'll need to be prepared for answering questions, managing your time, and using the test-taking strategies you've learned. It's a lot to balance, like a mental marathon that will have a big impact on your future. Like training for a marathon, you'll need to start slowly and work your way up. When test day arrives, you'll be ready.

Start with the strategies you've read in the first two Secret Keys—plan your course and study in the way that works best for you. If you have time, consider using multiple study resources to get different approaches to the same concepts. It can be helpful to see difficult concepts from more than one angle. Then find a good source for practice tests. Many times, the test website will suggest potential study resources or provide sample tests.

Practice Test Strategy

If you're able to find at least three practice tests, we recommend this strategy:

Untimed and Open-Book Practice

Take the first test with no time constraints and with your notes and study guide handy. Take your time and focus on applying the strategies you've learned.

Timed and Open-Book Practice

Take the second practice test open-book as well, but set a timer and practice pacing yourself to finish in time.

Timed and Closed-Book Practice

Take any other practice tests as if it were test day. Set a timer and put away your study materials. Sit at a table or desk in a quiet room, imagine yourself at the testing center, and answer questions as quickly and accurately as possible.

Keep repeating timed and closed-book tests on a regular basis until you run out of practice tests or it's time for the actual test. Your mind will be ready for the schedule and stress of test day, and you'll be able to focus on recalling the material you've learned.

Secret Key #4 – Pace Yourself

Once you're fully prepared for the material on the test, your biggest challenge on test day will be managing your time. Just knowing that the clock is ticking can make you panic even if you have plenty of time left. Work on pacing yourself so you can build confidence against the time constraints of the exam. Pacing is a difficult skill to master, especially in a high-pressure environment, so **practice is vital**.

Set time expectations for your pace based on how much time is available. For example, if a section has 60 questions and the time limit is 30 minutes, you know you have to average 30 seconds or less per question in order to answer them all. Although 30 seconds is the hard limit, set 25 seconds per question as your goal, so you reserve extra time to spend on harder questions. When you budget extra time for the harder questions, you no longer have any reason to stress when those questions take longer to answer.

Don't let this time expectation distract you from working through the test at a calm, steady pace, but keep it in mind so you don't spend too much time on any one question. Recognize that taking extra time on one question you don't understand may keep you from answering two that you do understand later in the test. If your time limit for a question is up and you're still not sure of the answer, mark it and move on, and come back to it later if the time and the test format allow. If the testing format doesn't allow you to return to earlier questions, just make an educated guess; then put it out of your mind and move on.

On the easier questions, be careful not to rush. It may seem wise to hurry through them so you have more time for the challenging ones, but it's not worth missing one if you know the concept and just didn't take the time to read the question fully. Work efficiently but make sure you understand the question and have looked at all of the answer choices, since more than one may seem right at first.

Even if you're paying attention to the time, you may find yourself a little behind at some point. You should speed up to get back on track, but do so wisely. Don't panic; just take a few seconds less on each question until you're caught up. Don't guess without thinking, but do look through the answer choices and eliminate any you know are wrong. If you can get down to two choices, it is often worthwhile to guess from those. Once you've chosen an answer, move on and don't dwell on any that you skipped or had to hurry through. If a question was taking too long, chances are it was one of the harder ones, so you weren't as likely to get it right anyway.

On the other hand, if you find yourself getting ahead of schedule, it may be beneficial to slow down a little. The more quickly you work, the more likely you are to make a careless mistake that will affect your score. You've budgeted time for each question, so don't be afraid to spend that time. Practice an efficient but careful pace to get the most out of the time you have.

Secret Key #5 – Have a Plan for Guessing

When you're taking the test, you may find yourself stuck on a question. Some of the answer choices seem better than others, but you don't see the one answer choice that is obviously correct. What do you do?

The scenario described above is very common, yet most test takers have not effectively prepared for it. Developing and practicing a plan for guessing may be one of the single most effective uses of your time as you get ready for the exam.

In developing your plan for guessing, there are three questions to address:

- When should you start the guessing process?
- How should you narrow down the choices?
- Which answer should you choose?

When to Start the Guessing Process

Unless your plan for guessing is to select C every time (which, despite its merits, is not what we recommend), you need to leave yourself enough time to apply your answer elimination strategies. Since you have a limited amount of time for each question, that means that if you're going to give yourself the best shot at guessing correctly, you have to decide quickly whether or not you will guess.

Of course, the best-case scenario is that you don't have to guess at all, so first, see if you can answer the question based on your knowledge of the subject and basic reasoning skills. Focus on the key words in the question and try to jog your memory of related topics. Give yourself a chance to bring the knowledge to mind, but once you realize that you don't have (or you can't access) the knowledge you need to answer the question, it's time to start the guessing process.

It's almost always better to start the guessing process too early than too late. It only takes a few seconds to remember something and answer the question from knowledge. Carefully eliminating wrong answer choices takes longer. Plus, going through the process of eliminating answer choices can actually help jog your memory.

Summary: Start the guessing process as soon as you decide that you can't answer the question based on your knowledge.

How to Narrow Down the Choices

The next chapter in this book (**Test-Taking Strategies**) includes a wide range of strategies for how to approach questions and how to look for answer choices to eliminate. You will definitely want to read those carefully, practice them, and figure out which ones work best for you. Here though, we're going to address a mindset rather than a particular strategy.

Your odds of guessing an answer correctly depend on how many options you are choosing from.

Number of options left	5	4	3	2	1
Odds of guessing correctly	20%	25%	33%	50%	100%

You can see from this chart just how valuable it is to be able to eliminate incorrect answers and make an educated guess, but there are two things that many test takers do that cause them to miss out on the benefits of guessing:

- Accidentally eliminating the correct answer
- Selecting an answer based on an impression

We'll look at the first one here, and the second one in the next section.

To avoid accidentally eliminating the correct answer, we recommend a thought exercise called **the $5 challenge**. In this challenge, you only eliminate an answer choice from contention if you are willing to bet $5 on it being wrong. Why $5? Five dollars is a small but not insignificant amount of money. It's an amount you could afford to lose but wouldn't want to throw away. And while losing $5 once might not hurt too much, doing it twenty times will set you back $100. In the same way, each small decision you make—eliminating a choice here, guessing on a question there—won't by itself impact your score very much, but when you put them all together, they can make a big difference. By holding each answer choice elimination decision to a higher standard, you can reduce the risk of accidentally eliminating the correct answer.

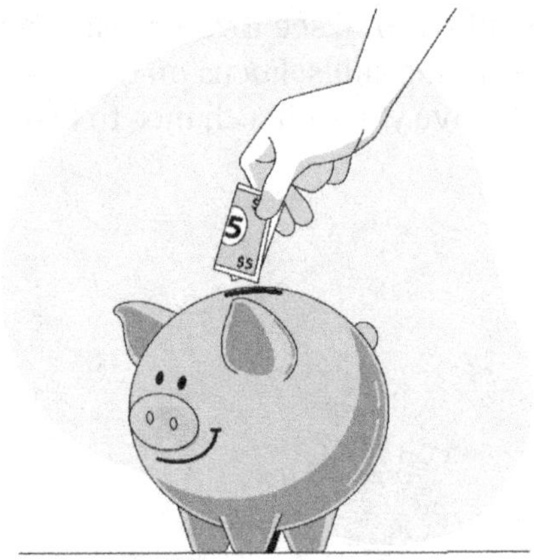

The $5 challenge can also be applied in a positive sense: If you are willing to bet $5 that an answer choice *is* correct, go ahead and mark it as correct.

Summary: Only eliminate an answer choice if you are willing to bet $5 that it is wrong.

Which Answer to Choose

You're taking the test. You've run into a hard question and decided you'll have to guess. You've eliminated all the answer choices you're willing to bet $5 on. Now you have to pick an answer. Why do we even need to talk about this? Why can't you just pick whichever one you feel like when the time comes?

The answer to these questions is that if you don't come into the test with a plan, you'll rely on your impression to select an answer choice, and if you do that, you risk falling into a trap. The test writers know that everyone who takes their test will be guessing on some of the questions, so they intentionally write wrong answer choices to seem plausible. You still have to pick an answer though, and if the wrong answer choices are designed to look right, how can you ever be sure that you're not falling for their trap? The best solution we've found to this dilemma is to take the decision out of your hands entirely. Here is the process we recommend:

Once you've eliminated any choices that you are confident (willing to bet $5) are wrong, select the first remaining choice as your answer.

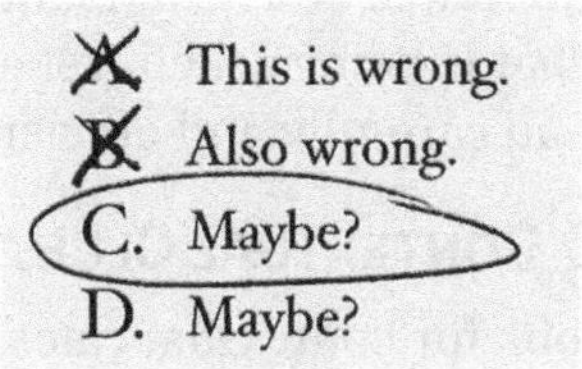

Whether you choose to select the first remaining choice, the second, or the last, the important thing is that you use some preselected standard. Using this approach guarantees that you will not be enticed into selecting an answer choice that looks right, because you are not basing your decision on how the answer choices look.

This is not meant to make you question your knowledge. Instead, it is to help you recognize the difference between your knowledge and your impressions. There's a huge difference between thinking an answer is right because of what you know, and thinking an answer is right because it looks or sounds like it should be right.

Summary: To ensure that your selection is appropriately random, make a predetermined selection from among all answer choices you have not eliminated.

Test-Taking Strategies

This section contains a list of test-taking strategies that you may find helpful as you work through the test. By taking what you know and applying logical thought, you can maximize your chances of answering any question correctly!

It is very important to realize that every question is different and every person is different: no single strategy will work on every question, and no single strategy will work for every person. That's why we've included all of them here, so you can try them out and determine which ones work best for different types of questions and which ones work best for you.

Question Strategies

READ CAREFULLY

Read the question and the answer choices carefully. Don't miss the question because you misread the terms. You have plenty of time to read each question thoroughly and make sure you understand what is being asked. Yet a happy medium must be attained, so don't waste too much time. You must read carefully and efficiently.

CONTEXTUAL CLUES

Look for contextual clues. If the question includes a word you are not familiar with, look at the immediate context for some indication of what the word might mean. Contextual clues can often give you all the information you need to decipher the meaning of an unfamiliar word. Even if you can't determine the meaning, you may be able to narrow down the possibilities enough to make a solid guess at the answer to the question.

PREFIXES

If you're having trouble with a word in the question or answer choices, try dissecting it. Take advantage of every clue that the word might include. Prefixes can be a huge help. Usually, they allow you to determine a basic meaning. *Pre-* means before, *post-* means after, *pro-* is positive, *de-* is negative. From prefixes, you can get an idea of the general meaning of the word and try to put it into context.

HEDGE WORDS

Watch out for critical hedge words, such as *likely, may, can, sometimes, often, almost, mostly, usually, generally, rarely*, and *sometimes*. Question writers insert these hedge phrases to cover every possibility. Often an answer choice will be wrong simply because it leaves no room for exception. Be on guard for answer choices that have definitive words such as *exactly* and *always*.

SWITCHBACK WORDS

Stay alert for *switchbacks*. These are the words and phrases frequently used to alert you to shifts in thought. The most common switchback words are *but, although*, and *however*. Others include *nevertheless, on the other hand, even though, while, in spite of, despite*, and *regardless of*. Switchback words are important to catch because they can change the direction of the question or an answer choice.

✓ Face Value

When in doubt, use common sense. Accept the situation in the problem at face value. Don't read too much into it. These problems will not require you to make wild assumptions. If you have to go beyond creativity and warp time or space in order to have an answer choice fit the question, then you should move on and consider the other answer choices. These are normal problems rooted in reality. The applicable relationship or explanation may not be readily apparent, but it is there for you to figure out. Use your common sense to interpret anything that isn't clear.

Answer Choice Strategies

✓ Answer Selection

The most thorough way to pick an answer choice is to identify and eliminate wrong answers until only one is left, then confirm it is the correct answer. Sometimes an answer choice may immediately seem right, but be careful. The test writers will usually put more than one reasonable answer choice on each question, so take a second to read all of them and make sure that the other choices are not equally obvious. As long as you have time left, it is better to read every answer choice than to pick the first one that looks right without checking the others.

✓ Answer Choice Families

An answer choice family consists of two (in rare cases, three) answer choices that are very similar in construction and cannot all be true at the same time. If you see two answer choices that are direct opposites or parallels, one of them is usually the correct answer. For instance, if one answer choice says that quantity x increases and another either says that quantity x decreases (opposite) or says that quantity y increases (parallel), then those answer choices would fall into the same family. An answer choice that doesn't match the construction of the answer choice family is more likely to be incorrect. Most questions will not have answer choice families, but when they do appear, you should be prepared to recognize them.

✓ Eliminate Answers

Eliminate answer choices as soon as you realize they are wrong, but make sure you consider all possibilities. If you are eliminating answer choices and realize that the last one you are left with is also wrong, don't panic. Start over and consider each choice again. There may be something you missed the first time that you will realize on the second pass.

✓ Avoid Fact Traps

Don't be distracted by an answer choice that is factually true but doesn't answer the question. You are looking for the choice that answers the question. Stay focused on what the question is asking for so you don't accidentally pick an answer that is true but incorrect. Always go back to the question and make sure the answer choice you've selected actually answers the question and is not merely a true statement.

✓ Extreme Statements

In general, you should avoid answers that put forth extreme actions as standard practice or proclaim controversial ideas as established fact. An answer choice that states the "process should be used in certain situations, if…" is much more likely to be correct than one that states the "process should be discontinued completely." The first is a calm rational statement and doesn't even make a definitive, uncompromising stance, using a hedge word *if* to provide wiggle room, whereas the second choice is far more extreme.

⊘ Benchmark

As you read through the answer choices and you come across one that seems to answer the question well, mentally select that answer choice. This is not your final answer, but it's the one that will help you evaluate the other answer choices. The one that you selected is your benchmark or standard for judging each of the other answer choices. Every other answer choice must be compared to your benchmark. That choice is correct until proven otherwise by another answer choice beating it. If you find a better answer, then that one becomes your new benchmark. Once you've decided that no other choice answers the question as well as your benchmark, you have your final answer.

⊘ Predict the Answer

Before you even start looking at the answer choices, it is often best to try to predict the answer. When you come up with the answer on your own, it is easier to avoid distractions and traps because you will know exactly what to look for. The right answer choice is unlikely to be word-for-word what you came up with, but it should be a close match. Even if you are confident that you have the right answer, you should still take the time to read each option before moving on.

General Strategies

⊘ Tough Questions

If you are stumped on a problem or it appears too hard or too difficult, don't waste time. Move on! Remember though, if you can quickly check for obviously incorrect answer choices, your chances of guessing correctly are greatly improved. Before you completely give up, at least try to knock out a couple of possible answers. Eliminate what you can and then guess at the remaining answer choices before moving on.

⊘ Check Your Work

Since you will probably not know every term listed and the answer to every question, it is important that you get credit for the ones that you do know. Don't miss any questions through careless mistakes. If at all possible, try to take a second to look back over your answer selection and make sure you've selected the correct answer choice and haven't made a costly careless mistake (such as marking an answer choice that you didn't mean to mark). This quick double check should more than pay for itself in caught mistakes for the time it costs.

⊘ Pace Yourself

It's easy to be overwhelmed when you're looking at a page full of questions; your mind is confused and full of random thoughts, and the clock is ticking down faster than you would like. Calm down and maintain the pace that you have set for yourself. Especially as you get down to the last few minutes of the test, don't let the small numbers on the clock make you panic. As long as you are on track by monitoring your pace, you are guaranteed to have time for each question.

⊘ Don't Rush

It is very easy to make errors when you are in a hurry. Maintaining a fast pace in answering questions is pointless if it makes you miss questions that you would have gotten right otherwise. Test writers like to include distracting information and wrong answers that seem right. Taking a little extra time to avoid careless mistakes can make all the difference in your test score. Find a pace that allows you to be confident in the answers that you select.

✓ KEEP MOVING

Panicking will not help you pass the test, so do your best to stay calm and keep moving. Taking deep breaths and going through the answer elimination steps you practiced can help to break through a stress barrier and keep your pace.

Final Notes

The combination of a solid foundation of content knowledge and the confidence that comes from practicing your plan for applying that knowledge is the key to maximizing your performance on test day. As your foundation of content knowledge is built up and strengthened, you'll find that the strategies included in this chapter become more and more effective in helping you quickly sift through the distractions and traps of the test to isolate the correct answer.

Now that you're preparing to move forward into the test content chapters of this book, be sure to keep your goal in mind. As you read, think about how you will be able to apply this information on the test. If you've already seen sample questions for the test and you have an idea of the question format and style, try to come up with questions of your own that you can answer based on what you're reading. This will give you valuable practice applying your knowledge in the same ways you can expect to on test day.

Good luck and good studying!

Final Notes

Good luck and good studying!

Exam Content/Registration

ARRT
http://www.arrt.com

Click on examinations/content specs

Scheduling the exam:
http://www.vue.com/arrt/

http://www.vue.com/arrt/

The American Registry of Radiologic Technologists®
1255 Northland Drive
St. Paul, Minnesota 55120-1155 USA
Phone (651) 687-0048

Patient Care

Ethical and Legal Aspects

Information to Collect from Patient Before Receiving Outpatient or Inpatient Services

The radiograph is not the only important part of a radiographic procedure. It is also important to obtain an accurate patient history when a radiographic procedure is conducted. It provides the radiologist with information necessary for accurately reading and interpreting the radiograph.

The information that should be collected from a patient before receiving services is as follows:

- Outpatient Services
    - Pregnancy information for women of childbearing age
    - Whether or not the patient did everything asked of them prior to the procedure
    - The reason that the patient is in for the procedure
    - Length of time that the patient has been experiencing problem
    - Visible signs of injury, illness, or pain/discomfort
    - Patient medications (particularly ones that may interfere with the image)
- Inpatient Services
    - Patient consent for the procedure
    - Date of any previous procedure
    - Labs and results relevant to the procedure
    - Medications that may adversely affect results (and prevent the procedure)
    - Patient condition that could prevent the procedure
    - Any patient information that may have an impact on the treatment

Patient Comfort

Radiographic procedures can be uncomfortable due to equipment and positioning. This can be made worse by the illness or injury of the patient. It is the responsibility of radiographic personnel to ease discomfort as much as possible. This includes the use of cushions, pillows, and sponges, as well as positioning considerations. A radiographer should also attend to basic patient needs such as allowing them going to the bathroom (and assisting when necessary), providing drinking water, warm blankets, a damp cloth, lip balm, and necessary personal cleanliness. If the patient is uncomfortable in any way, they are more likely to move and movement can compromise the quality of the image making a repeat procedure necessary. Thus, by making a patient as comfortable as possible, you enhance both the patient's experience and the quality of the image.

Informed Consent

Informed consent is communication between a patient and a healthcare provider that results in the patient giving the provider permission to perform a specific medical procedure. Informed consent means the patient has received comprehensive information about his or her diagnosis, the procedure to be performed, the risks of the procedure, alternatives to the procedure and their risks and the risks of not having the treatment or procedure. As part of informed consent, the patient should be permitted to ask questions to gain a thorough understanding of the recommended treatment. Informed consent is an ethical obligation and legal requirement in all 50 states.

Even if a physician writes a request to perform a radiological procedure, an informed consent is necessary before the procedure can be done. Legally, only a physician can get consent from the patient to do a procedure. This is because it is believed that it is the physician who is qualified to provide the patient with all of the necessary information (risks vs. benefits). This, however, is not always the case. It is still important for radiology personnel to provide the patient with thorough information regarding the procedure, particularly if there are any risks involved. With invasive or risky procedures, it is necessary to get written consent from the patient before the procedure is done.

Exceptions

There are some exceptions to the rule of informed consent. They are as follows:

- Emergencies: If the patient's life is at stake, they are unconscious, and the procedure is widely accepted a necessary for treatment, there is no need to get informed consent.
- Emotional Distress/not able to process information: Informed consent is not necessary if a patient is unable to understand the information given to him by the doctor, whether it is because of a mental handicap or the patient has become emotionally distraught.
- Legal Incompetence: Informed consent is waived if a judge rules a patient incompetent.
- Minor Age Status: Informed consent may be waived if the patient is a minor and getting parental consent is not a possibility. If the procedure is not a matter of life or death, it may be postponed until a legal guardian can consent to it.

Requirements

In order for a procedure to be performed, the ordering doctor must provide the patient with all necessary information and get their consent to have it done. The following are the requirements for getting informed consent for a procedure:

- The physician ordering the procedure got consent to do so from the patient.
- Risk/Benefit information was provided to the patient.
- Other treatment possibilities were discussed with patient.
- Patient informed of possible outcome if the procedure is not done.
- Patient was informed using understandable language.
- The place that provided the service also provided patient with information about risks.
- State-mandated rules regarding time between signing consent and performing procedure were followed.
- The patient was not scared or forced into having the procedure performed.

Confidentiality and Diagnosis/Interpretation

The American Society of Radiological Technologists has developed a code of ethics that acts as a guideline for the radiographer in completing their job in the best possible manner. Confidentiality and diagnosis/interpretation are important aspects of this code of ethics. It is the responsibility of the radiographer to respect a patient's privacy and confidentiality. This includes any information about the procedure, diagnosis, medical or personal history. The only exception to this policy is legally required information. It is also the responsibility of the radiographer to understand the scope and limitations of their profession. It is absolutely not the job of a radiographer to provide interpretations or diagnosis. Even if years of experience yield extensive knowledge and abilities, the radiographer should never overstep these bounds.

HIPAA

HIPAA is the Health Insurance Portability and Accountability Act approved by congress and signed into law in 1996. HIPAA was enacted to protect the privacy of personal health information by setting limits on the use and disclosure of such information without patient authorization. The Act also gives patients' rights over their health information, including the right to examine and obtain copies of their health records and the right to request corrections.

Patient Privacy

Every patient has a right to privacy during a procedure. The basics of patient privacy for a radiographic procedure are as follows:

- Provide a private area for changing or dressing.
- Provide a dressing gown that has closures (use two gowns if the patient is large).
- Cover the patients' exposed legs and feet. Provide slippers if necessary.
- Only expose parts of the body that are necessary for the procedure.
- Allow only necessary personnel in the room during the procedure.
- Do not have personal conversations with other personnel in front of the patient.
- Show the patient's chart to only necessary personnel and do not discuss the patient with others.
- Respect patient confidentiality.

Patient's Rights

Even if a physician writes an order to perform a procedure, it is ultimately up to the patient to decide if the procedure will be performed. Every patient has the right to refuse any medical procedure. This patient's right, among others, stems from the Patient's Bill of Rights. In 1973, the American Hospital Association developed the first Patient's Bill of Rights. It was a document that outlined a patient's rights when it comes to choices in healthcare. This Bill of rights has been updated and adopted, in some form, by most states, and it is the responsibility of the radiographer to become familiar with their local version. It covers topics such as informed consent, advanced directives, living wills, appointment of surrogates, confidentiality, privacy, access to medical records, and access to healthcare.

Advance Directives

In accordance to Federal and state laws, individuals have the right to self-determination in health care, including decisions about end of life care through **advance directives** such as living wills and the right to assign a surrogate person to make decisions through a durable power of attorney. Patients should routinely be questioned about an advanced directive as they may present at a healthcare provider without the document. Patients who have indicated they desire a do-not-resuscitate (DNR) order should not receive resuscitative treatments for terminal illness or conditions in which meaningful recovery cannot occur. Patients and families of those with terminal illnesses should be questioned as to whether the patients are Hospice patients. For those with DNR requests or those withdrawing life support, staff should provide the patient palliative rather than curative measures, such as pain control and/or oxygen, and emotional support to the patient and family. Religious traditions and beliefs about death should be treated with respect.

Beneficence and Nonmaleficence

Beneficence is an ethical principle that involves performing actions that are for the purpose of benefitting another person. In the care of a patient, any procedure or treatment should be done with the ultimate goal of benefitting the patient, and any actions that are not beneficial should be reconsidered. As conditions change, procedures need to be continually reevaluated to determine if they are still of benefit.

Nonmaleficence is an ethical principle that means healthcare workers should provide care in a manner that does not cause direct intentional harm to the patient:

- The actual act must be good or morally neutral.
- The intent must be only for a good effect.
- A bad effect cannot serve as the means to get to a good effect.
- A good effect must have more benefit than a bad effect has harm.

Requirements for Research Participation

Research participation requires precise documentation for every step, not only for the subject's safety and rights but also to protect the validity of the study being conducted. The pretrial documentation should include the brochures for the trial and how they recruited subjects, compensation, certificates that outline how products will be shipped along with their purity, and signed consent forms. During the trial, standard operation procedure (SOP) and specific protocols should be in place along with the confidential list of participants and any records pertaining to the patient's care (e.g., prescriptions, labs, radiology exams, and notes kept by the subject). After the trial, a case study is produced explaining the results of the trial. It is communicated if subjects will need follow-up care, and all supplies are accounted for and returned to the vendor. All of the documentation should be the original paperwork that was filed during the trial. If the original files cannot be provided, a certified copy should be used. The paperwork should also have signatures to identify who filed the paperwork along with the dates.

Risk Management in Relation to Legal and Professional Responsibilities

Because of all of the potential legal issues regarding negligence within the medical field, risk management has become an important way for medical institutions to minimize liability and risk. Incident reports are used to document any problems or questionable incidents that occur in a department. If an incident report is filed, it does not necessarily mean that a person is admitting guilt or that supervisors view the staff involved as guilty. It is simply a clear and consistent way to document just what happened in an incident that has the potential for future investigation. If anything, it can protect medical personnel if a patient charges negligence.

TQI and TQM in Relation to Legal and Professional Responsibilities

TQI (total quality improvement) and TQM (total quality management) are ways to measure and manage the quality of service as a means to reduce liability and risk. They look at the quality of service as a function of productivity. Many businesses, not just healthcare, use TQI and TQM to improve quality and productivity. In healthcare, it is a way to cut costs without sacrificing service. It does not, however, take into consideration the human nature of healthcare. Every patient is different and has different needs. It is important that the radiographer follows department protocol for quality improvement and productivity, but always keeps in mind individual patient needs and the code of ethics.

Request to Perform an Examination

Before any radiographic procedure is conducted, it is necessary to have a formal request from a doctor. The request may be written, faxed, or verbal. The submission of a request is the first step in a radiological procedure. The request should include all of the necessary patient information such as name, age, date of birth, medical number, patient type, date of last menstrual period (when appropriate), the physician, and the type of procedure to be done. This last bit of information is, perhaps, the most important. Without it, the radiographer does not know what needs to be done. If there is any question regarding the order, it is the responsibility of the radiographer to contact the ordering physician to get a clarification.

Proper Patient Identification

Proper patient identification is important because it can prevent a critical error like misidentifying a patient specimen which could result in harm or death to a patient. Patient identification includes asking a patient to state their name and date of birth, and then you check the identification band and the requisition to see if they match. Verbal identification should never be relied on alone although it is important since patients can be hard of hearing, ill, or mentally incompetent and may give incorrect information. Also, check the identification band since it is possible for a patient to be wearing the wrong ID band. If there is no ID band, notify the nurse and have her confirm the patient's identity and attach an ID band before the blood is drawn. If there is any discrepancy on the ID band, information given by the patient or on the requisition, a reconciliation of the discrepancy must be made before a collection is taken. More than one patient may have the same name. Usually a name alert is placed on the chart but not in all cases.

Negligence

There are four parts to negligent behavior: duty, breach of duty, causation, damages. Behavior is termed negligent when a radiographer does not correctly or adequately perform a previously outlined duty that results in harm (or potential harm) to the patient. The key is that the duty must be defined. If harm befalls a patient while under the care of a radiographer, their actions will be carefully analyzed to see if there was any negligence on the part of the radiographer. Even if no harm befalls a patient, a radiographer can be considered negligent if proper procedure has not been followed and there was a potential for harm. Thus, it is not only important that the radiographer is well informed of proper procedure, but that the procedure is followed.

Civil Liability

It is the ethical and legal responsibility of the radiographer to do their job in an accurate and professional manner. If not, the radiographer may be held responsible for negligence and be demanded by the courts to compensate the patient for damages. This responsibility is referred to as civil liability and is determined by a series of intentional torts (civil wrongs done on purpose with the intent to interfere with a person's physical freedom). Intentional torts are battery (not getting consent from the patient to touch them, acting in a way that injures or harms the patient), assault (threatening an uncooperative patient), false imprisonment (unnecessarily restraining a patient), intentional infliction of emotional distress (extreme behavior that causes emotional distress), and defamation (providing false information about a patient).

Subpoena Duces Tecum

Subpoena duces tecum literally means bring [it] with you under penalty of punishment. It is a court order for a witness to produce documents. The judge must carefully consider if *subpoena duces tecum* transgresses the patient's HIPAA rights.

Handling Wounds of Violence and Child Abuse

The physician and other health professionals must report to authorities:

- Gunshot wounds
- Possible terrorist incidents, especially if they involve the spread of disease
- Known or suspected abuse of a child, senior, or disabled person
- Sexual assault of a juvenile or disabled person

- Poisoning
- Wounds intentionally caused by knives and sharp objects
- Criminal violence, including domestic violence
- Client-specific information for the central cancer registry
- Specific contagious diseases determined by each state

Good Samaritan Act and Duty of Care

There are two kinds of Good Samaritan Acts:

- A first aider who provides unpaid assistance to the injured in an emergency and acts as "a reasonable man" up to his/her level of training is protected by state law from unfair prosecution for death, disability, or disfigurement. A judge would dismiss assault and battery charges. A *Good Samaritan Act* is not a duty to assist law, except in Vermont and Minnesota. Nevada and California may adopt a duty to assist clause.
- A living donor who offers a non-directed donation of an organ to the transplant center is a Good Samaritan. The following organs can be donated by a living donor: kidneys; liver lobes; lung lobes; pancreas segments; and small bowel segments. Non-direct donors do not have anyone particular in mind whom they would like to receive their donated organ. The donation is usually anonymous and the Good Samaritan is blameless for complications the recipient suffers.

Duty of care: One must act as "a reasonable man" and meet the standard of care to avoid negligence charges. This means being watchful, attentive, cautious, and prudent at work.

Restraints

Restraint policies vary from one facility to another, but their purpose remains the same.

- Restraints are applied in order to protect the patient from causing harm to himself or to other people.
- A restraint may be applied to prevent the patient from interfering with medical devices or moving in a way that would be detrimental to his health.
- It may also be applied if the patient is showing signs of aggression.
- A restraint should always be applied after all other alternatives have been exhausted.

It should not be applied as a form of punishment or for the convenience of the staff.

Prior to applying a restraint, all other alternatives must be exhausted. The health care staff must attempt to identify and address the behaviors that require the application of restraints.

- An order from the patient's physician must be obtained in order to apply restraints, and the physician should visibly assess the patient within 24 hours of the time of application of the restraints.
- Consent should be obtained from the patient's next of kin.
- Care must be taken to choose the least restrictive form of restraint.
- The type of restraint should be explained to the patient, as well as the reasons for the application of the restraint and the requirements for removal of the restraint.

ALTERNATIVES

There are a number of measures that can be performed as an alternative to applying restraints. The type of alternatives that are utilized may vary depending upon the patient. Any needs should be assessed and all reasonable alternatives performed prior to application of restraints.

- The patient may need to be moved to a quiet environment.
- He may require more stimulation, such as hearing a television or radio in the background.
- He may require redirection.
- The patient may need toileting or water.
- He may need personal items placed within reach.
- He may require distraction if the care team is attempting to remove a medical device.
- If the patient has an illness or requires rest, it may cause him to act in a manner that is confused or inappropriate.

APPLYING RESTRAINTS TO EXTREMITIES

Extremity restraints are applied to the arms and legs to restrict movement. A doctor's order and consent from the family must be obtained prior to application of these restraints.

- The nurse aide should wash her hands and don a pair of gloves.
- She should greet the patient and explain the need for the restraint, as well as the requirements for removal.
- The restraint should be applied per the manufacturer's instructions and tied to the frame of the bed using a quick release knot.
- The patient should be given a reasonable amount of slack in order to move.
- The nurse aide should be able to fit two fingers between the patient's extremity and the restraint; this ensures that is it not too tight.

MONITORING PATIENTS

Patients who are in restraints should be closely monitored to ensure safety.

- They should be checked every 30 minutes to make sure there is proper circulation.
- While they are restrained, patients should have their legs covered with a blanket in order to maintain privacy.
- The restraint should be removed every 2 hours to allow for range of motion.
- Patients should also be repositioned for comfort and offered water and toileting every two hours.
- Teaching regarding the restraints should be frequently reinforced to encourage patient understanding of the need for the restraint and the requirements for removal.

SECURING RESTRAINTS TO A WHEELCHAIR VERSUS A BED

When securing restraints on a patient who is in a wheelchair, care should be taken to ensure the restraint is tied using a quick release knot attached directly to the frame of the wheelchair. The wheelchair should be locked, and care should be taken to ensure the restraints are not tied to the wheels.

Similarly, when the patient is in bed, the restraint should be tied using a quick release knot attached directly to the frame of the bed. Tying the restraint to the side rail can cause injury to the patient if the side rail should fall.

Types

There are a number of different types of restraints that can be used in a health care setting.

- Emotional restraints are a method of using verbal or emotional cues in order to attempt to modify the patient's behaviors. This can include limit setting or contracting with the patient for safety.
- Environmental restraints are devices used to restrict patient movement. These include side-rails on the bed or locked doors within the facility. When all four side-rails are in a raised position on the bed, it is considered to be a restraint.
- Physical restraints are devices that can be applied to the patient to restrict movement. These include wrist and vest restraints, lap belts, and movement pads.
- Chemical restraints are medications that are given to the patient to modify behavior.

Vest Restraints

A vest restraint is a device that is placed over the patient's chest to restrict movement. It is typically applied to prevent a patient from getting up without assistance. A doctor's order and consent from the family must be obtained prior to application of the restraint.

- The nurse aide should wash her hands and don a pair of gloves.
- She should greet the patient and explain the need for the restraint, as well as the requirements for removal.
- The vest restraint should be placed on the patient so that the opening is toward the back, with the straps crossing in the back.
- The straps should then be tied with a quick release knot directly to the chair or the frame of the bed.
- At least two fingers should be able to fit beneath the vest restraint to ensure that it is not too tight.
- Once the restraint has been applied, remove the gloves and wash your hands.
- Monitor the patient per facility policy.

Immobilization of Patient During CT

The positioning and immobilization of the patient during CT is crucial if the practitioner is to obtain an accurate reading. The positioning should be conducive to replication because the treatment machine can reproduce the virtual simulation parameters in the event that a follow-up or second screening becomes necessary. Devices provided for immobilization and registered to the treatment table allow practitioners to position the patient correctly for the different scans required for each study, usually ranging from 100 to 200 scans. Diagnostic CT scanners are fitted with external laser alignment systems and virtual simulation software that allow practitioners to study the patient from a beam's eye view (BEV) and a room's eye view (REV) display. Digitally reconstructed radiographs (DRRs), multiplanar reformatted images (MPRs), and digitally composited radiographs (DCRs) can also be produced by the CT scanner, although these technological advances are not useful if the patient is not properly immobilized during the test.

Potential Legal Issues Regarding Manipulation of Electronic Data

Exams performed in the radiology department are part of the patient's legal file (whether they are captured on film or digital equipment). To provide the correct diagnosis for a patient the technologist must make sure that the name of the patient is on the film as well as the date. Technologists must verify they have the correct patient prior to performing any exam. Another legal requirement is that technologists must utilize their lead markers with their identifying initials on the films even if using equipment. It is important to use collimation as any digital masking or shuttering performed after the exposure has been taken may not be admissible in court. It is important that the technologist doesn't rely on post-processing techniques to create an image. Technologists must be even more cautious of the as low as reasonably achievable (ALARA) principle when using digital radiography equipment. Extensive knowledge of techniques is important so that one does not overexpose patients. Technologists should be familiar with acceptable exposure indicator ranges for the different vendors used in a department.

Principles of ASRT Code of Ethics

The American Society of Radiological Technologists has developed a code of ethics that acts as a guideline for the radiographer in completing their job in the best possible manner. The ten principles of this code of ethics are as follows:

- Act in a professional manner.
- Respect the dignity of everyone.
- Deliver healthcare without discrimination.
- Be a competent technician.
- Make decisions that take into consideration the needs of your patients.
- Diagnosis and interpretation are not your job or responsibility.
- Be aware of and practice current technical and safety procedures.
- Practice ethical behavior that provides quality care.
- Respect patient privacy and confidentiality.
- Be involved in continuing education.

Important Terms

DNR: Do not resuscitate. No codes should be called for this patient and no heroic measures should be taken to revive patient if the patient stops breathing.

NPO: From the Latin phrase nil per os meaning nothing by mouth. Patients are not allowed food or drink including water. This restriction is usually placed on a patient before and after a procedure.

STAT: From the Latin word statim means immediately. It describes the need for a specimen or test to be done immediately in response to critical situations with the possibility of the test results preventing a patient's death.

ASAP: As soon as possible, this is used if the results are needed soon but not to prevent the patient from dying

Fasting: When a person refrains from eating or drinking anything before a procedure, sometimes water is allowed on a fast

Statute of Limitations: A law defining the maximum period the complainant or appellant can wait before filing a lawsuit. The limitation date varies according to the type of case and if it falls within state or federal jurisdiction. Usually, the limitation is 1 to 6 years. Homicide has no limitation. If the complainant misses the deadline, then the right to sue is "stats barred" (dead). Rarely, a judge will "toll" (extend) the deadline if the injury was discovered late or a trusted person hid misuse of funds or failure to pay. Minors' rights to bring negligence charges are tolled until the age of 18.

Assumption of Risk: (A.) A defense against an accusation of negligence. The defendant states the situation was obviously hazardous, so the complainant should have realized injury could result. (B.)

An insurance company takes the risk of extending coverage, realizing the policyholder might make a claim, but it is statistically more likely to make a profit from the premiums.

Arbitration Agreement: The patient agrees to give up the right to sue the doctor. An arbiter (arbitrator) awards damages if injury results. Settlement is faster for the patient, and the doctor gets a malpractice insurance discount. Both parties save on legal fees.

Negligence: Taking an unreasonable, careless action that could foreseeably cause harm. Failing to exercise due care for others that a prudent, reasonable person would do. Negligence is accidental. Negligence is not an intentional tort, such as trespass or assault. Business errors, miscalculations, and failure to act can be negligent.

Contributory Negligence: If a person is injured partially because of his/her own negligence: even if it is slight: then the person who caused the accident does not pay any damages (money) to the injured person. Forty-four states recognize that applying the rule of contributory negligence could lead to unfair acquittal of genuinely negligent defendants, so they now use a comparative negligence test as a more balanced approach. In the 6 states that still have contributory negligence rules, juries tend to ignore it as unfair.

Comparative Negligence: A rule used in accident cases to calculate the percentage of responsibility of each person (joint tortfeasors) directly involved in the accident. Damages (money compensation) are awarded based on a complex formula.

Defamation: Defaming a person exposes him or her to public ridicule or tarnishes his or her memory through untrue and malicious statements. The defamed person can lose business due to loss of his or her good name.

Slander: Oral statements that damage someone's reputation. It is a form of defamation.

Libel: A written statement that harms an individual's character, name, or reputation. A defamatory libel statement may be true, but is published maliciously (without just cause).

Invasion of Privacy: Unsolicited or unauthorized exposure of patient information.

Malpractice: Professional misconduct, resulting in failure to provide due care. Most malpractice lawsuits are related to professional negligence, the failure to perform what is considered standard care.

Fraud: Intentional dishonesty for unfair or illegal gain.

Assault and Battery: Assault is declaring or threatening your intent to touch a patient inappropriately or to cause physical harm. Battery is thc actual act of inappropriate touching.

Subpoena: A legal writ (order) requiring a person to come to court, to testify in court, and/or to produce documents or evidence. Failure to do so may result in fine or jailing.

Res Ipsa Loquitur ("the thing speaks for itself"): The principle of law that allows the use of circumstantial evidence as proof.

Locum tenens ("to substitute for"): Allows one medical professional to serve temporarily in place of another. For example, a physician's practice may be covered by another physician usually for a few days up to 6 months when the first goes on vacation or takes leave. Companies specialize in providing locums physicians to work on a contract basis.

Deposition: This is a sworn out-of-court witness statement taken under oath, usually in an attorney's office prior to a court case to document what the witness knows and to preserve the statements for use in court.

Stare Decisis ("to stand on the decisions"): It expresses the common law doctrine that court decisions should be guided by precedent.

Respondeat Superior ("let the master answer"): A doctrine in tort law that makes a master liable for the wrong of a servant; specifically, the doctrine making an employer or principal liable for the wrong of an employee or agent if it was committed within the scope of employment or agency.

Communicable Infection: An illness caused by the direct or indirect transmission of a specific infectious agent or the toxins it produces from an infected person, animal, or inanimate host to a susceptible body; indirect transmission can be via a vector, intermediate plant or animal host, or the inanimate environment.

Nosocomial Infection: Hospital-acquired illness not resulting from the original reason for the patient to be admitted.

Lumen: Lumen is the hollow area within a blood vessel

Valves: Valves are tissue flaps inside a vein or the heart that prevent backward flow of blood. Valves open as blood moves through them and close under the weight of blood collecting in the vein due to decreased pressure and gravity.

Interpersonal Communication

Verbal and Nonverbal Modes of Communicating

Because the radiographer is usually the only person to have contact with a patient during a radiographic procedure, it is important that they effectively communicate all important information, collect the necessary patient history, as well as make the patient feel as comfortable as possible. This is all done using various verbal and nonverbal modes of communication. The verbal ways that we communicate with others are obvious-we ask questions, provide information, clarify misunderstandings. Some of the ways that we communicate nonverbally are less obvious, yet equally as important. Nonverbal communication ranges from the organization and cleanliness of the radiographer and the radiography room, to the ways in which the patient is touched or transferred for the procedure. It is important to convey to the patient an attitude of understanding, caring, and competency.

Importance of Nonverbal Communication

Any type of message transmitted between two people that does not involve words is nonverbal communication. 85% to 93% of successful communication depends on nonverbal cues. Remember that your patient is likely apprehensive and English may not be his/her first language. Your patient may have difficulty speaking due to injury, drugs, age, deformity, developmental disability, or the instruments used during a procedure. Watch your patient's facial expressions, gestures, posture, and position. Tight posture and/or crossed arms and legs suggest resistance. Conversely, relaxed posture and uncrossed appendages suggest openness. Your posture affects your patient. Sit closely beside your patient, rather than towering directly over him/her in an intimidating manner. Explain what you are going to do. A patient feels more comfortable when he/she is well informed. Maintain the proper social distance (territoriality) between yourself and your patient during discussions (about 3 feet apart).

Cultural Considerations with Patients

Hispanic Patients

Many areas of the country have large populations of **Hispanic** and Hispanic-Americans. As always, it's important to recognize that cultural generalizations don't always apply to individuals. Recent immigrants, especially, have cultural needs that the nurse must understand:

- Many Hispanics are Catholic and may like the nurse to make arrangements for a priest to visit.
- Large extended families may come to visit to support the patient and family, so patients should receive clear explanations about how many visitors are allowed, but some flexibility may be required.
- Language barriers may exist as some may have limited or no English skills so translation services should be available around the clock.
- Hispanic culture encourages outward expressions of emotions, so family may react strongly to news about a patient's condition, and people who are ill may expect some degree of pampering, so extra attention to the patient/family members may alleviate some of their anxiety.

Cultural Considerations with Hispanic Patients

Caring for **Hispanic** and Hispanic-American patients requires understanding of cultural differences:

- Some immigrant Hispanics have very little formal education, so medical information may seem very complex and confusing, and they may not understand the implications or need for follow-up care.
- Hispanic culture perceives time with more flexibility than American, so if parents need to be present at a particular time, the nurse should specify the exact time (1:30 PM) and explain the reason rather than saying something more vague, such as "after lunch."
- People may appear to be unassertive or unable to make decisions when they are simply showing respect to the nurse by being deferent.
- In traditional families, the males make decisions, so a woman waits for the father or other males in the family to make decisions about treatment or care.
- Families may choose to use folk medicines instead of Western medical care or may combine the two.
- Children and young women are often sheltered and are taught to be respectful to adults, so they may not express their needs openly.

Middle Eastern Patients

Caring for **Middle Eastern** patients requires understanding of cultural differences:

- Families may practice strict dietary restrictions, such as avoiding pork and requiring that animals be killed in a ritual manner, so vegetarian or kosher meals may be required.
- People may have language difficulties requiring a translator, and same-sex translators should be used if at all possible.
- Families may be accompanied by large extended families that want to be kept informed and whom patients consult before decisions are made.
- Most medical care is provided by female relatives, so educating the family about patient care should be directed at females (with female translators if necessary).
- Outward expressions of grief are considered as showing respect for the dead.

- Middle Eastern families often offer gifts to caregivers. Small gifts (candy) that can be shared should be accepted graciously, but for other gifts, the families should be advised graciously that accepting gifts is against hospital policy.
- Middle Easterners often require less personal space and may stand very close.

Cultural Considerations with Middle Eastern Patients

There are considerable cultural differences among **Middle Easterners,** but religious beliefs about the segregation of males and females are common. It's important to remember that segregating the female is meant to protect her virtue. Female nurses have low status in many countries because they violate this segregation by touching male bodies, so parents may not trust or show respect for the nurse who is caring for their family member. Additionally, male patients may not want to be cared for by female nurses or doctors, and families may be very upset at a female being cared for by a male nurse or physician. When possible, these cultural traditions should be accommodated:

- In Middle Eastern countries, males make decisions, so issues for discussion or decision should be directed to males, such as the father or spouse, and males may be direct in stating what they want, sometimes appearing demanding.
- If a male nurse must care for a female patient, then the family should be advised that *personal care* (such as bathing) will be done by a female while the medical treatments will be done by the male nurse.

Asian Patients

Caring for **Asian** patients requires understanding of cultural differences:

- Patients/families may not show outward expressions of feelings/grief, sometimes appearing passive. They also avoid public displays of affection. This does not mean that they don't feel, just that they don't show their feelings.
- Families often hide illness and disabilities from others and may feel ashamed about illness.
- Terminal illness is often hidden from the patient, so families may not want patients to know they are dying or seriously ill.
- Families may use cupping, pinching, or applying pressure to injured areas, and this can leave bruises that may appear as abuse, so when bruises are found, the family should be questioned about alternative therapy before assumptions are made.
- Patients may be treated with traditional herbs.
- Families may need translators because of poor or no English skills.
- In traditional Asian families, males are authoritative and make the decisions.

Cultural Considerations with Asian Patients

There are considerable differences among different **Asian** populations, so cultural generalizations may not apply to all, but nurses caring for Asian patients should be aware of common cultural attitudes and behaviors:

- Nurses and doctors are viewed with respect, so traditional Asian families may expect the nurse to remain authoritative and to give directions and may not question, so the nurse should ensure that they understand by having them review material or give demonstrations and should provide explanations clearly, anticipating questions that the family might have but may not articulate.

- Disagreeing is considered impolite. "Yes" may only mean that the person is heard, not that they agree with the person. When asked if they understand, they may indicate that they do even when they clearly do not so as not to offend the nurse.
- Asians may avoid eye contact as an indication of respect. This is especially true of children in relation to adults and younger adults in relation to elders.

CULTURAL COMPETENCE

Different cultures view health and illness from very different perspectives, and patients often come from a mix of many cultures, so the acute care nurse must be not only accepting of cultural differences but must be sensitive and aware. There are a number of characteristics that are important for a nurse to have **cultural competence:**

- **Appreciating diversity:** This must be grounded in information about other cultures and understanding of their value system.
- **Assessing own cultural perspectives:** Self-awareness is essential to understanding potential biases.
- **Understanding intercultural dynamics:** This must include understanding ways in which cultures cooperate, differ, communicate, and reach understanding.
- **Recognizing institutional culture:** Each institutional unit (hospital, clinic, office) has an inherent set of values that may be unwritten but is accepted by the staff.
- **Adapting patient service to diversity:** This is the culmination of cultural competence as it is the point of contact between cultures.

ADMINISTRATION OF BLOOD PRODUCTS AND JEHOVAH WITNESSES

Jehovah Witnesses have traditionally shunned transfusions and blood products as part of their religious belief. In 2004, the *Watchtower,* a Jehovah Witness publication presented a guide for members. When medical care indicates the need for blood transfusion or blood products and the patient and/or family members are practicing Jehovah Witnesses, this may present a conflict. It's important to approach the patient/family with full information and reasons for the transfusion or blood components without being judgmental, allowing them to express their feelings. In fact, studies show that while adults often refuse transfusions for themselves, they frequently allow their children to receive blood products, so one should never assume that an individual would refuse blood products based on the religion alone. Jehovah Witnesses can receive fractionated blood cells, thus allowing hemoglobin-based blood substitutes.

Basic blood standards for Jehovah Witnesses:

- ***Not acceptable:*** Whole blood: red cells, white cells, platelets, plasma
- ***Acceptable:*** Fractions from red cells, white cells, platelets, and plasma

THERAPEUTIC COMMUNICATION TECHNIQUES

HEARING IMPAIRED PATIENTS

Hearing impaired patients may have some hearing and may use hearing aids while **deaf** patients typically have little or no hearing. Some patients are able to use lip reading to various degrees, so one should always face the patient (at 3-6 feet) and speak slowly and clearly, using gestures (not excessively) to augment speech:

- Hearing impaired: Assistive devices (hearing aids, writing material) should be available and used during communication. Use a normal tone of voice and speak in short sentences. Minimize environmental noises.

- Deaf: If patients are deaf, sign language interpreters should be used for important communication (face the patient, not the interpreter). Assistive devices, such as writing materials, TDD phone/relay service, should be available for use. Always announce presence on entering a room by waving, clapping, tapping the foot (whatever works best for the patient). Ensure alarms have visual feedback (lights). Do not chew, smoke, or eat while speaking to the patient.

Visually Impaired Patients

Visual impairment is unrelated to intelligence or hearing, so one should speak with age-appropriate vocabulary in a normal tone of voice, facing the patient so one can observe facial expression. Depending on the degree of visual impairment the patient may not be able to see gestures or materials, so alternate forms of materials (braille handouts or enlarged text) or manipulatives must be considered. The field of vision may be impaired so that the patient sees shapes or has better vision in some areas than others, and one should try to position herself/himself for the patient's advantage. One should also announce his/her presence, explain actions and movement ("I'm putting your dressing supplies on the counter."), announce position ("I'm at your right side.") and always tell the patient if intending to touch the patient ("I'm going to take your blood pressure on your right arm").

Effective Communication with the Intellectually Disabled and Illiterate

Communicating with patients who are **intellectually disabled** can be challenging, and patients may have very different and individual responses, so observation of the patient must serve as a guide. Patients may be apprehensive and frightened, so one should maintain a friendly normal tone of voice and should speak with the patient often to establish rapport, even if the response is not clear. One should always ask the patient before touching his/her things. Initiating communication by talking about familiar things (family, pictures, the past) may be comforting for the patient. If responses are unclear or inappropriate, one can say, "I didn't understand that" but should not laugh or indicate frustration. Communicating with patients who are **illiterate** is not different than with most patients because the patients may be quite intelligent, but one should take care to explain procedures and provide verbal rather than written instructions.

Therapeutic Responses to Various Populations

Therapeutic responses include:

- Pediatric/Adolescent: Use vocabulary appropriate to age and encourage adolescents to make decisions whenever possible ("Which arm should I use?"). Avoid approaching young children too abruptly but chat with the child and caregiver to ease the child's fear. Explain in advance any actions to be taken, such as temperature or BP, and allow the child to see and hold the equipment when possible.
- Geriatric: Treat patients with respect, address them by their names ("Mrs. Jones") and avoid terms like "honey," and "dear." Be alert for barriers, such as hearing deficit, to communication, and encourage patients to ask questions and discuss concerns. Avoid rushing and interrupting and utilize active listening skills.
- Terminally ill: Avoid being excessively sympathetic ("You poor thing"), but remain patient and empathetic. Utilize active listening and allow patient time to express feelings or concerns. Understand that patients may be in pain, weak, frightened, nauseated, and/or depressed and may over-react or under-react.

Explaining Procedures to Patients

It is very important that the patient fully understands the procedure that is to be done. A patient cannot be expected to consent to a procedure that they do not understand. There are different ways that a radiographer can communicate the information to the patient. Because everyone has a different level of education and understanding of medical procedures, a radiographer must tailor their explanation to the patient's needs. The following steps should be taken to assure that the patient is adequately informed:

- Ask is the patient is familiar with the procedure.
- Find out if the procedure has already been explained to them.
- Provide a simple and concise explanation using language they will understand.
- Explain if the patient is to do anything during the procedure (not move, hold breath).
- Have the patient explain any important instructions back to you.
- Allow the patient to ask questions.

Communication Techniques When Assessing Understanding

Communication techniques used when assessing patient's understanding and communication include:

- <u>Reflection</u>: Refers to both the meaning of the patient's words and the emotions. If a patient states, "I understand how to monitor my blood pressure," a reflecting question might be: "You feel confident that you know how to take your blood pressure and when to notify the physician?"
- <u>Restatement</u>: Restates or paraphrases something a patient said, "I've been having dizzy spells for two weeks?" Restatement might be: "You've been having dizzy spells for 2 weeks."
- <u>Clarification</u>: Asks for more information. If a patient states, "I haven't been feeling well," a clarifying question might be: "What exactly do you mean when you say you haven't been feeling well?"
- <u>Feedback</u>: Responds to something a patient has said or done, letting them know that the message/information was received: "You have kept very accurate records of your blood pressure and pulse."

Common Internal and External Distractions That Disrupt Communication

Distractions (interference) that disrupt the communication cycle include:

- <u>Internal</u>: The communicator's or recipient's emotional status, such as increased anxiety or anger, can negatively impact communication. Biases, prejudices, and belief systems may also interfere with a person's ability to attend to the ideas of another person. Pain and hunger can be so distracting that the person is unable to focus on communication. When under stress, the brain may process information differently, interfering with comprehension.
- <u>External</u>: Noise in the environment (conversation, traffic, alarms, air conditioning) can make it hard for some people to hear clearly, especially those with hearing impairment, and may make concentration difficult. Additionally, people may find noise very stressful to the point that they have difficulty thinking. Other environmental factors, such as extremes of heat or cold, may cause physical discomfort that interferes with the ability to communicate.

Communication Techniques to Encourage in Therapeutic Relationships

The following are 4 *appropriate* communication techniques to encourage in therapeutic relationships:

- **Use active listening** – Paraphrase and repeat back information transmitted by your patient. Ask for clarification when the message is confusing. Summarize what you agreed to at the end of your conversation.
- **Watch for nonverbal cues** – Nonverbal cues are gestures, grimaces, posturing, appearance, and eye movements that comprise 85% of all communication. Nonverbal cues denote pain, fear, lying, depression, or subterfuge by a caregiver. Gently ask your patient to clarify when verbal and nonverbal cues do not match. Children and psychiatric patients may develop tic disorders (involuntary gestures and movements). If you cannot decipher which movements are truly cues and which are tics, ask the doctor.
- **Ask open-ended questions** – Get your patient to 'open up', rather than ask questions that require only a yes or no answer.
- **Consider influences** – Put communication in the context of your patient's: Developmental age; emotions; values; ethics; health; education; culture; environment; social and family status; and drug levels.

Inappropriate Communications Techniques

The following are 10 *inappropriate* communications techniques to avoid in therapeutic relationships:

- **Ask leading questions** – Never shape the patient's answers to questions, or try to change the patient's interpretation of the situation by "putting words into the patient's mouth"
- **Demand an explanation** – Do not ask "why" questions in an accusing tone
- **Give advice** – Only the physician advises
- **Demand an immediate response** – Allow the patient sufficient time for silent reflection before responding
- **Disinterested body language** – Do not appear distracted or make the patient feel inconsequential by impatient motions, bored posture, or rolling your eyes
- **Minimize the patient's feelings** – Do not compare feelings and experiences
- **Negatively empower** – Do not help your patient to manipulate another person
- **Make false promises** – Never promise the patient that the doctor will definitely cure the condition, or make promises that cannot be kept
- **Play into stereotypes** – Racist, sexist, and religious prejudice must not influence your treatment of the patient
- **Deliberately mislead** – Always disclose upcoming treatments, tests, or procedures

Pre- and Post-Examination Instructions

Some radiographic exams require patients to follow specific pre-exam instructions to better visualize the anatomy of interest. For example, patients may be asked to be NPO (take nothing by mouth including gum and smoking) eight hours prior to the exam. Others may require a colon prep starting the day before the exam to rid the body of excess waste to better visualize internal structures. Other times, the patient may need to be sedated, and it is important the patient is NPO so the patient does not aspirate. If patients are taking a medication to help them relax, they must be informed of exact times for the medication to be effective. Also, if patients have been sedated, it is important that they have somebody drive them home. Technologists should also be sure to give patients important post-exam instructions. For example, after barium studies the patient will need to drink a lot of liquids and take a mild laxative to prevent constipation. Patients should also be informed of how the results will be communicated to them (typically from the ordering physician's office).

MRI Procedures

MRI stands for magnetic resonance imaging and is a procedure that does not use ionizing radiation. Instead, it uses magnetic fields and computer software to produce an image. The dye gadolinium is used as a contrast medium for the procedure. MRI is particularly useful in imaging soft tissue. Because it does not used ionizing radiation, there are, in general, fewer risks associated with MRIs. However, because it uses magnetism, any metal objects in the room or on/in the patient can become sources of injury. Also, because an MRI must be conducted within a close distance to the patient, many people experience claustrophobia. It is sometimes necessary to medicate the patient so that they remain still long enough to get a quality image.

CT Procedures

CT stands for computed tomography and is a highly specific application of radiation and computer analysis that is used to get a detailed, three-dimensional image. Because the primary beam of radiation is highly collimated (restricted) and delivered in a helical (spiral) fashion using slip ring technology, it can be precisely targeted to the area of interest to provide a multi-layered image. An iodinated contrast medium allows for the visual differentiation of different tissues. In order to get the quality image necessary for diagnosis, it is very important that a patient remain still for a CT procedure. It is sometimes necessary to medicate the patient so that they remain still long enough to get a quality image.

Ultrasound Procedures

Ultrasound (or medical sonography) creates an image by recording the echo of sound waves as they bounce off the anatomy to which they are applied. It is primarily a non-invasive procedure that does not carry with it the risk of exposure to ionizing radiation. For this reason, it is the primary means of visualizing the fetus during pregnancy. It can, however, be used in invasive procedures such as biopsy, intravaginal imaging, transesophageal echocardiography. To improve imaging, water is sometimes consumed so that the full bladder acts to magnify the anatomy being imaged. This is particularly helpful in fetal imaging.

Nuclear Medicine Procedures

In nuclear medicine, instead of the patient being exposed to radiation externally, they are injected with a radioactive isotope. Once the body begins to emit gamma radiation, the image is captured by a scintillation camera and analyzed by a computer. Because of the potential danger in working with radioactive materials, only nuclear medicine technologists are authorized to inject the radioisotope. It is a procedure that is extensively regulated by the NRC (nuclear regulatory committee). A department must keep very accurate records and properly dispose of nuclear waste in order to maintain a license to practice nuclear medicine.

Mammography Procedures

Used to detect breast cancer, mammography uses tissue compression and low doses of radiation to image breast tissue. It has become a highly regulated area of radiography that requires additional training and continuing education. The Mammography Quality Control Standards Act (MQSA) of 1994 and American College of Radiology (ACR) regulations provide the guidelines for mammography use and interpretation. Because breast tissue can be difficult to image using mammography alone, ultrasound, nuclear medicine, and MRI combined with the use of a breast coil can help give more accurate results. A biopsy (surgical or needle) is used to confirm the presence of cancer. Appropriate film-screen combinations are necessary to get the best image. A computer image does not provide enough detail for an accurate diagnosis.

Procedures for 12-Lead ECG

An ECG (electrocardiogram) measures the electric impulses of the heart and is an indication of blood flow and heart operation. When placing a 12-Lead ECG, the patient should be laying down and covered with a sheet to maintain their basic privacy rights. The skin should be clean, dry, and devoid of hair. To improve conductivity, gel is applied to the skin before placing the lead. The leads are distributed between the limbs and chest. Proper placement is important in obtaining good results. If not placed properly, artifacts can result, obscuring the actual reading.

Physical Assistance and Monitoring

Proper Technique for Falling with a Patient

Even with all necessary precautions properly observed while ambulating, the patient is still at risk for falling. A fall may result if the patient's legs give out from under him or if he were to lose consciousness while ambulating. If a sudden fall were to occur, it is important to protect the patient and yourself from harm.

- Support the patient using the gait belt and your free arm, and gently lower the patient to the floor or to a nearby chair, taking care to protect the patient's head.
- If the fall is uncontrolled as a result of loss of balance, focus on supporting the patient as much as possible while keeping yourself safe.
- Try to avoid tensing up prior to impact as this may cause additional injury.

Proper Body Mechanics to Prevent Personnel and/or Patient Injury

Because patients are often ill or physically impaired and equipment can be heavy or bulky, it is important that a radiographer understands the basics of proper body mechanics so as not to injure themselves or the patient when moving a load. The basics of body mechanics are the same whether the load is a person or piece of equipment. Personnel must assess if the load can be lifted alone, with mechanical help, or with the help of another person. When moving anything, it is important to maintain a wide stance with a straight back and lift with the knees. Keeping the load close to your body and being sure that there is nothing that will impede movement will assure proper transfer of the load. When transferring a patient to or from a wheelchair or bed, always check to see if the wheel locks are set. Finally, make sure you clearly explain to the patient what you are going to do so that they do not hinder the move.

Devices to Promote Patient Safety

Common devices to promote patient safety include:

- **Lifts**: Utilizing lifts, such as the Hoyer lift, to assist in moving and lifting patients reduces the risk of falls and injuries.
- **Assistive devices**: Various assistive devices, such as canes, walkers, wheelchairs, grabbers, reaching devices, and medication dispensers, help to prevent falls, facilitate mobility, and promote safety.
- **Alarms**: Many types of sensors with alarms are available, including floor mat sensors, chair sensors, seatbelt sensors, and movement sensors. Door alarms may sound when doors are opened to alert staff.

- **Wander management systems**: Systems such as *Wanderguard®* and *RoamAlert®* require the patient to wear a device (such as a bracelet) that contains a locator and may also have a door controller to automatically lock doors as the patient approaches them or to sound alarm if the patient passes through an open door.

Patient Health Support

Vascular Access Devices

Many patients in need of a radiographic procedure have their health compromised in one or more ways. When a patient's health is compromised, any number of instruments or devices can be employed for patient health support. One such item is the use of vascular access devices (VADs). These are semi-permanent devices that allow access to a patient's veins to administer fluids, electrolytes, nutrients, and medications without having to stick the vein every time. They are used in chronically ill patients. The three types of VADs are central venous catheter (implanted into a large vein, usually the superior vena cava), percutaneous central venous catheter (implanted under fluoroscopic conditions into the subclavian vein), and implanted infusion port (surgically implanted into the infraclavicular fossa). All types of VADs must be kept clean and observed for the presence of infection. Care should be taken when moving a patient to not disturb or irritate the implantation site.

Oxygen

Many patients in need of a radiographic procedure have their health compromised in one or more ways. They may be critically ill, be suffering from injuries, or have an undiagnosed disease. When a patient's health is compromised, any number of instruments or devices can be employed for patient health support. One such item is the use of oxygen. Oxygen is a basic need for the functioning of the body. Most radiological suites have it available through ports in the wall; otherwise it is available in portable tanks. It is given to a patient in a humidified form (so as not to dry and irritate the throat and lungs) through a nasal cannula, oxygen mask, or mechanical ventilator. Flames or sparks should not be used in the presence of oxygen because of the possibility of combustion.

Intravenous Devices

Many patients in need of a radiographic procedure have their health compromised in one or more ways. They may be critically ill, be suffering from injuries, or have an undiagnosed disease. When a patient's health is compromised, any number of instruments or devices can be employed for patient health support. One such item is the use of intravenous devices. Commonly referred to as IV's, they are used to administer fluids, electrolytes, nutrients, and medications directly into the patient's bloodstream. Today, most IV fluids are administered using an IV pump. A radiographer needs to understand the basics of IV pump operation. Because every pump can be different, refer to pump instructions or consult nursing staff. The patient's chart must always be consulted before restarting an IV pump or replacing an empty bag so that the proper prescription is maintained.

Nasogastric Tube

Many patients in need of a radiographic procedure have their health compromised in one or more ways. They may be critically ill, be suffering from injuries, or have an undiagnosed disease. When a patient's health is compromised, any number of instruments or devices can be employed for patient health support. One such item is a nasogastric (NG) tube. This is a tube that is inserted into the nose, down the nasopharynx, into the stomach and is used to add or remove fluid in the stomach. If a radiographer uses the tube to administer contrast medium, water-soluble iodinated contrast medium (never barium) should be used. Care should be taken when working with a patient that has an NG tube so as not to disturb it.

Urinary Bladder Catheter

Many patients in need of a radiographic procedure have their health compromised in one or more ways. They may be critically ill, be suffering from injuries, or have an undiagnosed disease. When a patient's health is compromised, any number of instruments or devices can be employed for patient health support. One such item is a urinary bladder catheter (also called a Foley catheter). Inserted into the urinary bladder and attached to a bag, it is used to drain the patient's bladder. Some radiographic procedures require a full bladder, and so the catheter must be clamped and then unclamped for pre and postvoid films. Care should be taken when working with a patient that has urinary bladder catheter so as not to disturb it.

Closed-Chest Drainage Systems

Many patients in need of a radiographic procedure have their health compromised in one or more ways. They may be critically ill, be suffering from injuries, or have an undiagnosed disease. When a patient's health is compromised, any number of instruments or devices can be employed for patient health support. One such item is a closed-chest drainage system. It is used to remove air or fluid from the chest cavity after surgery or trauma. It helps prevent problems such as infection or a collapsed lung. Care should be taken when working with a patient that has a closed-chest drainage system so as not to disturb it. If fluid levels markedly increase or become bloody, nursing staff should be immediately notified.

Ostomy

If a patient's health is compromised, and any number of instruments or devices can be employed for patient health support. One such item is the use of an ostomy. It is a surgically created opening that allows for the exit of feces, urine or air from the patient's body. The different types of ostomies are: colostomy/enterostomy (opening through the abdominal wall into the colon for the removal of feces), ureterostomy (a procedure that brings the ureter up to the stomach for the removal of urine), ileal loop/incontinent urinary diversion (surgical movement of the ilium of the small bowel to the stomach for the removal of urine), continent urinary diversion (surgically implanted internal pouch that acts as a reservoir for urine). Care should be taken when working with a patient that has any form of ostomy so as not to disturb it. If a contrast medium is necessary, water-soluble iodinated contrast medium (never barium) should be used.

Tracheostomy

Many patients in need of a radiographic procedure have their health compromised in one or more ways. They may be critically ill, be suffering from injuries, or have an undiagnosed disease. When a patient's health is compromised, any number of instruments or devices can be employed for patient health support. One such item is the use of a tracheostomy. This is a surgical opening (tracheotomy) made into the trachea to allow for air flow into the patient's lungs. Many patients with a tracheotomy also require suction and oxygen, so it is important that a radiographer understands the use of both and has it available for use when necessary. Care should be taken when working with a patient that has a tracheotomy so as not to disturb it.

Suction

Many patients in need of a radiographic procedure have their health compromised in one or more ways. They may be critically ill, be suffering from injuries, or have an undiagnosed disease. When a patient's health is compromised, any number of instruments or devices can be employed for patient health support. One such item is the use of suction. It is used to remove fluid, blood, or mucus from a patient's airway. Like oxygen, it usually available in most radiological suites through a port in the wall. A disposable catheter is used to collect and dispose of secretions. The radiographer should be familiar with the use of suction in patients in case the need should arise (particularly in patients with a tracheotomy).

Patient Safety

It is important that all medical procedures are safe for the patient. The basics of patient safety for medical procedures are as follows:

- Be sure to properly identify the patient.
- Conduct patient needs assessment.
- Use proper body mechanics so as not to injure yourself or the patient.
- Use safety straps, side rails, and immobilization devices properly and when necessary.
- Be aware of the location of the patient when moving equipment.
- Properly label and store patient personal belongings.
- Document any patient injury or property loss/damage immediately.

Monitoring Patient's Health and Well-Being

Although a radiographer is not a nurse, it is important that they have an understanding of some of the basics of clinical nursing so that a consistent quality of care can be maintained during radiographic procedures. Many patients in need of a radiographic procedure have their health compromised in one or more ways. They may be critically ill, be suffering from injuries, or have an undiagnosed disease. Because a nurse cannot always accompany a patient during a radiographic procedure, the responsibility of routine monitoring of patients can fall to the radiographer. It is important that the radiographer can recognize the signs of failing health and knows how to respond to medical emergencies.

Monitoring Vital Signs and Other Patient Indicators During CT Scanning

The machinery used to perform CT often includes provisions for monitoring the patient's vital signs, such as blood pressure, heart rate, oral temperature, and oxygen saturation. The test can be more effective if these vital signs are kept within normal limits, and doctors can choose to discontinue testing if the vital signs vary from those normal limits in response to the contrast agent, the duration of the test, or other factors. Patients are usually requested not to eat or drink for at least 4 hours before testing, although this requirement may be waived in an emergency. Patients should also be informed about immobilization on a hard table, venipuncture, a salty taste in the mouth, redness of skin during dye injection, mild nausea, diarrhea, and allergic reaction or kidney failure, which occur only rarely. Some patients are given a sedative for relaxation and easing of claustrophobia.

Physical Signs and Symptoms to Monitor

Technologists should always monitor patients for any sign of reaction to contrast or any decline of health during a procedure. Specifically, has there been a change in the patient's level of consciousness? Is the patient alert enough to comprehend and answer questions asked? Are there any indications of hives or cyanosis when looking at the patient's skin? Is the patient's breathing of normal rate and rhythm? A patient's pulse ox can easily be monitored should the technologist find it necessary to check. Technologists should be aware of any seizures that the patient may experience. Blood pressure is yet another important vital sign to monitor along with heart rate to determine the severity of a reaction to contrast, when caring for trauma patients, or during routine monitoring of a patient during an exam. If intravenous contrast was used, check for any signs of extravasation.

Creating a Safe Workplace Environment

One should take an active role in creating a **safe workplace environment** and preventing accidents:

- Slips: Most slips occur when the floor is wet or lacks adequate traction. Common causes include spills (water, urine, soap), oily substances (leaking oil), loose rugs and mats, and excessive floor waxing. Slips are especially a risk during wet weather as people may track water or snow in from outside. Floors should be checked and kept clean and dry,
- Trips: Most trips occur when the foot encounters obstacles (wrinkled rugs, cables, cords, clutter), view/walkway is obstructed, or lighting is poor. Traffic areas should be kept clear of clutter and lighting checked. Uneven steps should have warning signs.
- Falls: Many falls result from slipping or tripping, but some occur from a height, such as from a ladder or stairs. Patients who are unstable should always be assisted when walking and assisted at an appropriate pace.

Importance of Fall Prevention

Patient falls are a considerable problem in the health care setting. Injuries resulting from a fall are considered to be a primary cause of morbidity in older adults. The loss of coordination and bone density as people age puts them at an increased risk for breaking bones after a fall; the resultant loss of independence may lead to a decline in health and eventual death. Yet falling is not a normal part of aging. Proper prevention can greatly decrease a patient's risk of falling. As a nurse aide, it is important to follow fall precautions to prevent patient falls within the hospital setting.

Review Video: Fall Prevention
Visit mometrix.com/academy and enter code: 972452

Safety for Bed-Bound Patients

Patients who are bedridden have a particularly high risk of falling. The following are necessary safety precautions for bed-bound patients:

- While the patient is in bed, make sure the side rails are up to prevent the patient from climbing out of bed.
- If necessary, a bed alarm may be placed in the bed to alert the nurse aide that the patient is attempting to get out of bed without assistance.
- The patient's call light should be placed within reach, as well as the patient's tray table and any other items the patient might need.
- Toileting should be offered at least every two hours, and the patient should be turned every two hours to prevent bedsores.

Precautions to Prevent Falls

There are a number of precautions that can be taken to prevent patient falls.

- The first step of prevention is identifying the needs of the patient.
- If the patient has been determined to be a fall risk, a sign should be placed on the door so the staff knows the patient has special mobility needs.
- While the patient is in bed, at least two side rails should be kept in the raised position to prevent the patient from falling out of bed.
- Prior to standing with assistance, patients should be allowed to sit or dangle at the side of the bed to prevent dizziness that may result from the change in position.
- The patient should also wear rubber-soled shoes or socks.

- The floor should be kept free of all hazards, including puddles of water and small rugs that can cause slipping.
- While the patient sits in or stands up from the chair or wheelchair, the brakes should be kept locked.

Proper Documentation of Routine Monitoring

Proper documentation must be performed to provide the best patient care possible during the exam. Documentation also provides pertinent information that may be reviewed by clinicians and staff when follow-up studies are to be performed. When injecting a patient with contrast during exams, it is important to document the contrast media, dose, and any reactions the patient experienced. Routine monitoring requires the technologist to check for any change in the patient's mental status or other important vitals. Many symptoms can be monitored just by looking at or speaking with the patient. If the patient is suddenly having difficulty breathing, sweating profusely, bleeding, developing hives, or having a hard time speaking because of laryngeal edema, these are all signs that he or she is having a reaction to the contrast.

Vitals Monitored During Sedation

Technologists must always monitor patients for any sudden change in health. During sedation even more attention must be given to make sure the patient is not reacting to any medication that has been given. Important vitals to monitor are body temperature, which should be between 98 °F and 99 °F. The patient's pulse should also be observed and should be between 60 and 100 beats per minute. Respiration should also be checked and be between 12 and 16 breaths per minute. The patient's blood pressure is another important vital sign that should be evaluated. If the diastolic number drops below 50, it is an indication that the patient is going into shock. If the same number rises above 90, then one can assume hypertension. If the patient is on oxygen, the typical range is between 2 and 5 liters per minute. Suction should always be available in case it is necessary to remove secretions from the patient's mouth or throat. A patient will be hooked up to an electrocardiogram (EKG) machine, and it is important to watch for any signs of cardiac arrest in addition to respiratory arrest.

Medical Emergencies

Patients who are hospitalized, seen in the emergency room, or treated on an outpatient basis should be monitored in case a medical emergency arises. All technicians and hospital personnel caring for patients should be trained in basic cardiac life support. In addition, the hospital should have an emergency response system and protocol in place that any technician and/or health care practitioner can initiate, which may involve a hospital emergency response team or protocol. Health care practitioners and technicians should be trained in the protocol and system to be put into effect if a medical emergency occurs when caring for or performing a diagnostic approach on a patient.

Management of Medical Emergencies

In most cases, if a patient is in critical condition, nursing or emergency staff will accompany a patient for a radiographic procedure. If a patient appears to be stable, however, nursing staff may not be immediately available and the radiographer may be called upon to react if an emergency arises. For this reason, the radiographer must be familiar with basic protocol in responding to common medical emergencies such as allergies, head injuries, shock, high/low blood sugar, nosebleed, seizures, cardiac arrest, and respiratory arrest. It may be necessary to initiate a life-saving procedure before nursing staff can respond or assist in the procedure once they do respond.

Allergic Reactions

An allergic reaction occurs when the body's acquired immune system has an adverse response to a substance (allergen). In order for the body to recognize the allergen, there is an initial exposure that does not cause a reaction, but sensitizes the body to the substance. It is a subsequent exposure to the allergen that then results in an allergic reaction (called an inflammatory response). The reaction can be a simple irritation caused by contact to the substance, a delayed allergic reaction, or an immediate allergic reaction. Some allergic reactions are serious and require immediate medical assistance. A severe allergic reaction has respiratory symptoms such as itchy eyes, runny nose, sneezing, wheezing, and difficulty breathing. A mild allergic reaction can cause skin redness, hives, or itching. Medical products that contain latex as well as the contrast media used in certain radiographic procedures can cause mild to severe allergic reactions in patients

Latex

Latex products can cause mild to sever allergic reactions in patients. The reaction can be to the proteins in the latex itself, or to the other chemicals added to latex in processing. There are three types of reactions that can occur when a person is sensitive to latex products:

- Irritant Contact Dermatitis – Mild skin irritation that is characterized by dry, itch areas. This is not considered a true allergic reaction.
- Allergic Contact Dermatitis – Also called delayed hypersensitivity. Usually occurs 24-48 hours after exposure. Causes a rash to oozing blisters.
- Latex Allergy – Also called immediate hypersensitivity. Occurs within minutes to hours after exposure. Reaction can be mild to serious.

Common medical equipment that could contain latex are disposable gloves, tourniquets, blood pressure cuffs, stethoscopes, IV tubing, oral and nasal airway tubing, enema tips, endotracheal tubes, syringes, electrode pads, catheters, wound drains, and injection ports.

Cardiopulminary Arrest

Cardiopulmonary arrest is a serious condition that occurs when there is a sudden stopping of blood and air flow within the body. Every radiographer must be trained in the "ABC's" (airway, breathing, circulation) of CPR and know how it differs depending on the age of the patient. If a patient appears to be going into cardiopulmonary arrest, stop the procedure immediately and call for help. Start CPR and proceed until the emergency team arrives. Don't simply wait until the emergency team arrives, doing nothing. Immediate treatment is necessary to save the patient's life.

Respiratory Arrest

Respiratory arrest is the failure of the lungs to fill with air. There are two types of respiratory arrest: acute and chronic. Acute respiratory arrest is caused by an airway obstruction, which requires the Heimlich maneuver to remove the obstruction or ineffective gas exchange in the lungs, which requires the use of positive pressure ventilation. Chronic respiratory arrest is due to the progress of a disease such as emphysema, bronchitis, or asthma and may require the use of ventilation or suction. It is important to recognize the difference between respiratory arrest (the patient stops breathing) and cardiopulminary arrest (there is no pulse as well as the cessation of breathing) so that the proper emergency procedure is followed.

Head Injuries

If a person has experienced any type of head injury, they should not be left alone. While they may initially seem stable, there is still a chance that they will need to vomit, and with this comes the possibility of choking on the vomitus (aspiration). If it is necessary to leave the room, make sure that someone is there to watch them while you are gone. If they need to vomit, provide them with an adequate container (like a large basin or bedpan). If they are lying down, turn them on their left side to vomit (the right side increases likelihood of choking). An individual with a head injury may also go into shock. It is necessary for a radiographer to know the signs and symptoms of shock.

Nosebleed

If a patient has a nosebleed, they should sit up if possible, otherwise raise their head. Use gauze to soak up the blood (not tissue), and have the patient apply pressure to the nasal septum. Applying ice to the nose is effective in constricting the blood vessels and slowing the flow of blood. The patient should be supplied with a basin to spit blood into and water for rinsing out their mouth. Bleeding should stop within ten minutes. If it does not stop within ten minutes or gets worse, call for medical assistance.

Seizures

If a patient experiences a seizure during a radiographic procedure, immediately stop the procedure and have the patient lie down. Cushion their head so as to minimize potential injury. To avoid choking, the patient should be turned on their left side; have suction and oxygen available and ready to use, should the need arise. Contrary to popular belief, they should not be restrained nor should anything be placed between their teeth. Monitor and time the duration of the seizure. When it is over, be sure to check the patient's vital signs.

Hypoglycemia

The key to responding to hypoglycemia (low blood sugar) is recognizing the signs and symptoms. These are tremors, sweating, sudden tiredness, hunger, syncope (fainting or dizziness). If hypoglycemia is suspected, first determine if the patient is a diabetic. If a glucometer is available and the patient is not rapidly failing, their blood sugar levels can be tested to determine if, indeed, it is hypoglycemia. To combat hypoglycemia, the patient needs to be given something that is sugary to eat. Glucose gel can be placed on the inner check, otherwise, orange juice or hard candy work well too. It typically takes 15 minutes to get the blood sugar levels back up. Once the episode is over, the patient's vital signs should be checked.

Shock

Shock can be the result of many different types of conditions. Because it can sometimes be serious, it is necessary for a radiographer to be familiar with the different types of shock. The causes of the different types of shock are as follows:

- Hypovolemic Shock: Low blood volume as a result of vomiting, diarrhea, hemorrhage
- Systemic Shock: Collapse of circulatory system as a result of intense infection
- Neurogenic Shock: Failure of arterial resistance due to head/spinal injury or neurotransmitter failure
- Cardiogenic Shock: Failure of the heart to pump due to pulmonary emboli (blood clot), myocardial infarct (heart attack), or pericardial edema (fluid around the heart)
- Anaphylactic Shock: Severe allergic reaction due to bee stings, medication, peanuts, or any foreign substance to which the body has not been exposed and sensitized.
- Syncope: Emotional response reaction due to fear, pain, or any severely unpleasant event.

Shock can be the result of many different types of conditions. Because it can sometimes be serious, it is necessary for a radiographer to be familiar with signs and symptoms of shock. Even though the different types of shock are caused by many different conditions, the signs and symptoms of shock are the same for all. They are as follows:

- Hypotension (low blood pressure)
- Tachycardia (pulse over 100 beats/minute)
- Skin that is cool, moist, and pale
- Increased rate of respiration
- Decrease in mental coherence
- Anxiety
- Thirst

If the radiographer notices any of the above signs and symptoms, they should stop the procedure immediately and call for help. The patient should be lowered to the ground with feet elevated. For the sake of the wellbeing of the patient, it is important to respond immediately. Recognizing that a patient is in shock, understanding how to call in a code, and knowing the location of the code cart are all important steps in saving a patient's life.

Infection Control

Bloodborne Pathogens

Bloodborne pathogens are microorganisms in the blood or other body fluids that can cause illness and disease in people. These microorganisms can be transmitted through contact with contaminated blood and body fluids. The majority of the population immediately refers to the HIV virus or AIDS when defining bloodborne pathogens. However, hepatitis B and C are much more common in the medical setting.

Exposure to Bloodborne Pathogens

A medical professional can be exposed to bloodborne pathogens by accidental puncture wounds from needles, scalpels, broken glass or razor blades. An individual can also be exposed if contaminated body fluids come into contact with an open wound on the skin. The hepatitis B virus can actually be transmitted indirectly when a medical professional touches dried or caked-on blood and then touches the eyes, nose, or mouth.

Cycle of Infection

The cycle of infection starts with the presence of a pathogen (a disease-causing organism) and an environment that allows it to grow and multiply. Aside from being able to grow and multiply, the conditions must allow it to be passed on (transmission) from one organism (host) to another. Transmission can be either direct or indirect. Direct transmission occurs when the infection is passed from one infected host to another. There are several different possible modes of indirect transmission. An object can become contaminated and a person becomes infected when they touch the contaminated object (called a fomite). A vector can be employed by the pathogen, infecting an intermediate host where it can multiply and develop before being passed on to a new host. The pathogen can become airborne before finding a new host to infect. In any mode of transmission, there must be a way for the pathogen to enter the new host and the host must be susceptible to the infection.

Reservoir

Medical professionals must understand all five components of the cycle of infection to prevent the spread of disease. All of these factors must be present for an infection to transpire. They are a reservoir host, exit mode, method of transmission, route of entrance, and a susceptible host. The first aspect takes place when a microorganism (pathogen) latches onto a living host. This living host is referred to as a reservoir host and may be a human, an insect, or even an animal. A reservoir's body will offer the proper nourishment for the pathogen for it to live and/or proliferate. When humans serve as the reservoir hosts, they become carriers of the disease but are often oblivious that they have been infected and can easily transmit the disease to other people. When there is evidence of a disease in a reservoir host, one may be more aware of hand washing and other methods to prevent the spread of disease.

Portal of Exit

The second step that must take place for an infection to occur is that the reservoir host provides a portal of exit. This describes the method in which the microorganism leaves the reservoir host to continue on to infect another organism, known as the susceptible host. The most prevalent avenues for exiting the body are via the mouth, nose, blood, urine, vaginal or seminal fluid, feces, and even the eyes. Often the portal of exit is the exact same as the entrance portals, which is the fourth step in the cycle of infection.

Method of Transmission

Droplet Mode of Transmission

Droplet (mucous) particles may be transmitted when the reservoir host sneezes or coughs. It is known that the reservoir host does not need to be in close proximity to the susceptible host as droplet particles can travel several feet in the air. Respiratory diseases such as influenza and tuberculosis may be transmitted via a direct airborne method when the susceptible host inhales the droplets of the infected person. These types of infections may sweep through a population rapidly, so it is important to practice proper techniques to prevent airborne transmission. This includes coughing or sneezing into a tissue when possible. If a tissue is not available, one should sneeze or cough into the crook of the elbow and then perform proper hand washing. Often, patients who have a respiratory infection are asked to wear a mask to prevent the spread of infected droplets.

Direct Contact Mode of Transmission

Bloodborne transmission may occur by direct mode if blood from the infected reservoir host comes into contact with the susceptible host's mucous membranes or when the integrity of the skin is compromised. Healthcare workers must always practice universal precautions and utilize personal protective equipment (PPE) such as gloves, gowns, masks, eye protection, and face shields to prevent blood from reaching these mucous membranes or from getting into any cut in the skin. The most common bloodborne pathogens that may be transmitted in a healthcare setting are hepatitis B (HBV), hepatitis C (HCV), and the human immunodeficiency virus (HIV). Healthcare professionals should assume and treat all bodily fluids as if they are contaminated, and any PPE should be managed and disposed of properly. Another example of direct transmission is when a pregnant female passes on a sexually transmitted infection (STI) onto her baby via the placenta or during a vaginal delivery, such as gonorrhea, herpes, or syphilis.

Airborne Mode of Transmission

The spread of microorganisms can take place when particles are dispersed from the respiratory system of the reservoir host and inhaled by another individual. This is known as airborne transmission. An example of airborne transmission is inhaling droplets when an infected individual coughs or sneezes. It is known that people do not need to be located right next to each other as these droplets are capable of traveling several feet following a cough or sneeze. This is a common method in which influenza, tuberculosis, or even chickenpox is spread. People may also become ill after the inhalation of bacteria or fungi within water that is contaminated. One example of this type of airborne infection is Legionnaires' disease. This is not spread from person to person but rather when somebody inhales water droplets that contain the bacteria. This is often heard of in contaminated water supplies such as in hotels, resorts, or air-conditioning systems of apartment complexes.

Vehicle-Borne Fomite Mode of Transmission

A fomite is referred to any inanimate object that can spread a pathogen from one person to the next. Common examples of fomites that aid in the transmission of disease are doorknobs, drinking fountains, water glasses, pens, toys, books, and shopping carts. With these examples, it is easy to see why schools or child-care centers can readily spread germs among individuals. Note that this transmission is carried out in an indirect fashion as body membranes do not need to touch each other. Examples of vehicle-borne fomites in the medical industry could be instruments used in clinical care settings such as tools used for surgical procedures or patient care. Other examples of a vehicle-borne fomite in the medical field could be blood, biopsy specimens, or organs and tissues used for transplants or grafting material.

Vector-Borne Mechanical or Biological Mode of Transmission

A vector-borne method of transmission occurs when pathogens are spread from one living organism to another. Vectors are commonly insects that act as couriers that transport bacteria and other common pathogens from one individual to the next. Examples of vectors are mosquitoes, flies, ticks, and fleas. Mosquitoes are known for spreading West Nile virus. Flies can mechanically transmit disease as they continuously land on food and people. Infected ticks are widely known for spreading Lyme disease when they bite a person. Another disease that ticks may spread is Rocky Mountain spotted fever, which may be deadly if not diagnosed correctly. Fleas are the culprits in transferring pathogens that allow people and animals to contract the plague. Mosquitoes, ticks, and fleas tend to fall under the biological mode of transmission as they tend to become infected because they feed on the blood of their hosts.

Portal of Entry

A portal of entrance is the fourth step that must take place for an infection to occur known as the cycle of infection. As the microorganism exits the reservoir host, it must have an entrance portal to infect the susceptible host. Examples of entrance portals are similar to exit routes and include any mucous membrane such as the nose, mouth, rectum, or vagina. These pathogens can also enter via the integumentary system when the skin is no longer intact. The eyes are yet another entrance portal, and conjunctivitis is a very contagious disease that is spread via this entrance method. Urinary tract infections are another common infection seen, especially in females. This occurs as bacteria from the rectum are transferred to the urethra because of the close proximity of these structures. It is important to practice proper hygiene whether it is wiping after using the toilet or hand washing to prevent the transfer of bacteria and other pathogens.

Susceptible Host

A susceptible host is the fifth and final component in the cycle of infection. A susceptible host is an individual that is unable to fight off an infection and will enable the cycle to continue when this individual passes the pathogen onto another person. There are many factors that determine whether the susceptible host will become infected. These may include the strength of the immune system, overall health, and level of nourishment. Age is another important factor as infants and the elderly are more susceptible to certain diseases. Hygiene practices as well as living conditions are yet another determining factor that may induce an infection. For example, perhaps the host employs great hand-washing techniques but is forced to wash with water that is contaminated while living in a house with rodents and insects. Sometimes the susceptible host, regardless of how healthy he or she is, may be infected with a microorganism so potent that the host is unable to fight it off even with a strong immune system.

Aseptic and Sterile Techniques of Venipuncture

During the physical act of administering medication, the practitioner should be aware of the basic tenets of sterilization. The medication or contrast agent must be injected with consideration for power injectors, other comparable methods, extravasation and treatment, and use of an IV pump. Any adverse reactions to contrast dyes, latex, or sedation and the treatment required for such reactions should be analyzed and included in the patient's documentation. The practitioner should always adhere to aseptic techniques and should verify that the area is free of pathogenic microorganisms so that infection can be prevented, according to the standards and guidelines set forth by the medical facility in which the venipuncture is being performed. All medical facilities must meet certain health codes regarding asepsis.

Surgical Asepsis

In order to prevent or control the spread of infection, the cycle of infection must be broken. The cycle of infection refers to the conditions that allow infection to spread. These conditions (presence of pathogen, growth and reproduction, transmission to host, susceptibility of host) must all be present in order for an infection to exist. Surgical asepsis (also called sterile technique) is a strict process of keeping an area sterile by removing any microorganisms from objects in the environment. This is done with the use of an autoclave, gas sterilization, or chemical cleaning solution. The area is then kept sterile by protecting it from contamination with the use of sterile draping, masks, caps, gowns, and gloves. Surgical asepsis should be used any time a patient is cut open for a procedure, if there is damaged skin (burns, cuts), or if a medical device is being inserted into a patient.

There are basic principles that govern surgical asepsis. They are in place to help keep an environment sterile, thus preventing and controlling the spread of infection. The most important (and basic) principle is that sterile objects remain sterile only when they come into contact with other sterile objects. No matter how clean the object it comes into contact with is, if it is not sterile, it should be considered a contaminant. If you are not sure if an object is sterile, or if the object is out of your field of view, it should be treated as contaminated.

Disinfectants and Antiseptics

Disinfectants are used to kill possible pathogens. They are bactericidal corrosive compounds composed of chemicals. Some disinfectants are capable of killing viruses such as HIV and HBV. These are not used on humans to disinfect skin. A common disinfectant is bleach in a 1:10 dilution.

Antiseptics are chemical compounds that inhibit or prevent the growth of microorganism microbes usually applied externally. Antiseptics attempt to prevent sepsis but do not necessarily kill bacteria and viruses. Antiseptics are used on human skin. Common antiseptics include70% isopropyl alcohol, betadine, and benzalkonium chloride with isopropyl alcohol being the most commonly used. Betadine is used when a sterile draw is needed.

Equipment Disinfection

The majority of supplies utilized in clinical settings tend to be disposable, but for those that can be reused, they must be properly disinfected or sterilized prior to another procedure. There are different levels of disinfection, but high-level disinfection is used when the equipment used has possibly been exposed to human immunodeficiency virus (HIV), hepatitis B virus (HBV), or hepatitis C virus (HCV). The steps for proper disinfection are as follows: remove equipment from the patient, remove any protective cover from the equipment, wipe off any excess fluid, rinse under water while using a soap containing a germicidal solution, immerse (when allowed) equipment into disinfecting agent for the suggested time (check equipment manufacturer for suggested disinfection solutions), rinse with water, and dry. Caution must be taken to allow enough time between patients for the equipment to be properly disinfected.

Equipment Sterilization

Equipment must be sterilized if it will be used during any procedure that requires a sterile field. Instruments that can be sterilized are typically stainless steel and hold up well to sterilization techniques to be used again. The most common method of sterilization for tools used in the medical industry is an autoclave. This method utilizes steam and pressure to rid the tools of any microorganisms that are present. Once a procedure has ended the tools must first be rinsed, sanitized, and dried per the department's protocols. Some tools must then be wrapped in a special paper that is porous enough for the moisture to reach the tools or placed in special pouches that may be placed in the autoclave. The autoclave typically has presets that can be chosen pertaining to the materials used. Once the cycle is finished, be sure to place the tools in a cool, dry place, and be cognizant of the expiration date as many will expire after 30 days.

Medical Asepsis

In order to prevent or control the spread of infection, the cycle of infection must be broken. The cycle of infection refers to the conditions that allow infection to spread. These conditions (presence of pathogen, growth and reproduction, transmission to host, susceptibility of host) must all be present in order for an infection to exist. Medical asepsis (also called clean or aseptic technique) refers to cleanliness practices in a non-sterile environment. The point is to remove as many pathogens as possible from the environment and prevent the spread of those that do exist. The biggest thing that can be done in medical asepsis is the washing of hands. The basic technique of hand washing is the use of warm water, antiseptic cleaner, the removal of jewelry, and specific cleaning of fingernails. Hands should be washed before and after contact with a patient, after contact with organic materials or contaminated equipment, after removing sterile or non-sterile gloves.

Sterile Technique

Method 1

The practitioner should scrub a selected area for 30 seconds with a sterile swab that is saturated in a 0.7% aqueous scrub solution of iodophor compound; any excess foam should be removed with another sterile swab. The iodophor complex solution should be applied with a sterile swab beginning at the intended venipuncture site and using gradually increasing concentric circles until an area 3 inches in diameter has been covered. The solution should be allowed to stand for 30 seconds before venipuncture is completed. If the practitioner cannot complete the venipuncture immediately after the 30-second waiting period, then the area should be covered with dry sterile gauze. If the arm is bent or the prepared site is touched by fingers or any other nonsterile object, the entire procedure for sterilization must be repeated.

Method 2

Another method of administering contrast agents requires scrubbing a selected area for 30 seconds with a sterile swab that is saturated in nonalcoholic, 15% aqueous soap or detergent solution so that any fat, oils, extra skin cells, dirt, and other debris can be cleaned away. The soap froth can be removed with another sterile swab saturated in 10% acetone in 70% isopropyl alcohol. The site should then be allowed to dry. A tincture of iodine can be applied with another sterile swab beginning at the venipuncture site and using gradually increasing concentric circles until an area 3 inches in diameter has been covered. The site should then be allowed to dry. The iodine can be removed with a sterile swab saturated in 10% acetone in 70% isopropyl alcohol, which should be allowed to dry. The prepared area should be covered with dry sterile gauze if the venipuncture is not completed immediately. If the arm is bent or the site is contaminated, the entire procedure must be repeated.

Method 3

For patients sensitive to iodine, the practitioner can directly apply 1 mL (an amount approximately the size of a penny) of One Step Gel to the venipuncture site. Held at an angle of approximately 30°, the sterile applicator can be used to scrub in a circular motion for 30 seconds until an area 1 inch in diameter directly over the venipuncture site has been covered. The same applicator can then be used, beginning at the intended venipuncture site and using gradually increasing concentric circles, to cover an area 3 inches in diameter. A second sterile applicator can be used to remove excess gel, beginning at the center of the 3-inch area and using gradually increasing concentric circles. The site should be allowed to dry according to the manufacturer's instructions. If the practitioner cannot complete the venipuncture immediately, the area should be covered with dry sterile gauze. If the arm is bent or the site is otherwise contaminated, the entire procedure must be repeated.

Method 4

Method 4 is the only method for sterilization of the intended injection site that does not require application in gradually increasing concentric circles from the intended venipuncture site. A solution of 2% chlorhexidine gluconate in 70% isopropyl alcohol should be prepared in advance. The practitioner should scrub the intended site of venipuncture with this solution, making repeated back-and-forth strokes across an area 2.5 inches by 2.5 inches for a minimum of 30 seconds. This repeated motion should ensure that the area is completely wet with the antiseptic. The area should be allowed to air dry for at least 30 seconds. If the practitioner cannot complete the venipuncture immediately, then the area should be covered with dry sterile gauze. If the arm is bent or the site is otherwise contaminated, the entire procedure must be repeated.

Universal/Standard Precautions for Prevention and Control of Infection

Universal (also called standard) precautions were developed in 1991 when, to help prevent and control the spread of infection, OSHA (Occupational Health Administration) and the CDC (Centers for Disease Control) mandated that every patient and specimen be treated as if it is contaminated. These precautions apply to all blood and bodily fluids (including peritoneal, amniotic, vaginal, seminal, cerebrospinal, synovial and saliva, pleural and pericardial fluids). Care should be taken when handling any of these fluids, or items contaminated with these fluids. Personal protective equipment (PPE), hand washing, and preventative measures should be employed.

Isolation and Infection Control Practices

There are isolation and infection control practices that should be completed with every radiographic procedure. They are as follows:

- Wash hands before and after each patient.
- Change pillowcase and clean the table surface between patients.
- Place a sheet on table surface to help keep it clean.
- Provide a denture cup for patient.
- Put the cassette in a pillowcase to keep it clean.
- Clean contaminated surfaces immediately.
- Clean equipment before reverse isolation procedures.

- Wear appropriate barrier dress (mask, gown, gloves).
- Properly dispose of protective gear and contaminated materials.

Safe Injection Practices

The Centers for Disease Control (CDC) recommends healthcare facilities practice the following guidelines to reduce the risk of exposure to patients and staff. First, aseptic protocols should always be followed during sterile procedures. If there is any question that the sterile field has been compromised, it is imperative to start over. Healthcare professionals must understand that syringes, needles, tubing, and so on are to be used on only one patient. A needle cannot be changed on a syringe after the syringe has already been used on another or even to draw up other medications for the same patient. All supplies used for an IV are to be properly discarded after being used on one patient. Medication and solutions should be dispensed to a patient from single-dose vials. If there is residual medication, it should not be given to another patient from the same single-dose ampule. For more information please refer to the CDC website https://www.cdc.gov.

Safe Handling of Contaminated Equipment and Surfaces

There are levels of disinfection for contaminated medical equipment and surfaces. These factors largely depend on equipment manufacturer guidelines and whether the supplies can be heat sterilized. High-level disinfection is one method that can be used for equipment that cannot be sterilized with heat, but it is not appropriate for surface disinfection. Regardless of which level necessary, all items are to be rinsed, sanitized, and then per the vendor's suggestions utilize only the disinfecting agents mentioned. Products used for high-level disinfection are considered to be sporicidal agents, are extremely virulent, and should also be rinsed with water and dried after the chemicals are used. Intermediate-level disinfection will kill tuberculosis but will not be effective at eliminating the bacterial spores. Low-level disinfection is used for surface areas and instruments such as stethoscopes, blood pressure cuffs, electrocardiogram (EKG) leads and wires, and so on that do not touch the mucous membranes of the patient.

Disposal of Biohazardous Materials

Biohazardous materials include anything that has been soiled with blood or other bodily fluids. They must be placed in special biohazard waste receptacles so that they can then be disposed of properly. Sharps must be placed in the designated sharps container. Radioactive material must be allowed to decay before being disposed of. None of these items are a part of the normal trash pick-up. In fact, facilities spend large sums of money on biohazardous waste disposal. Heavy fines are the result if not disposed of properly. Biohazardous waste disposal is regulated by the EPA (Environmental Protection Agency), OSHA (Occupational Health Administration), and NRC (Nuclear Regulatory Committee).

Prevention and Control of Infection

Droplet, Airborne, and Reverse Isolation Precautions

Droplet isolation precautions should be used when coming into contact with diseases that are spread by droplets (includes meningitis, Mycoplasma pneumonia, rubella, group A strep). Patients should be placed in private rooms. Masks and gloves must be worn when treating the infected patient, and gloves worn when coming into contact with every patient. Airborne isolation precautions should be used for tuberculosis, measles, and varicella. These are diseases that are spread by microscopic particles that must be filtered out of the air with special equipment. Patients must be completely isolated in negative pressure rooms. Contact precautions (gloves, gowns) must be employed and respiratory masks worn when in the infected patient's room. Reverse isolation precautions are designed to protect a patient from the healthcare worker. They are employed in cases when a patient is immunocompromised (leukemia patient, organ transplant patient). These patients should be isolated in positive pressure rooms that keep outside air and contaminants away from them.

Contact Isolation Precautions

Standard/Universal precaution measures should always be used when coming into contact with patients and bodily fluids. Certain diseases, however, require more stringent isolation precautions because of their highly contagious nature. Infections of MRSA, Salomonella, E. coli, hepatitis A, severe herpes simplex, lice, and scabies all require contact isolation precautions. These precautions require that gloves and gown always be used when entering the patient's room. Gloves must be changed when they come into contact with infectious material. Essentially, there should always be a barrier (gloves, mask, gown) between you and the patient, and the barrier material must be disposed of properly

Handling and Disposal of Toxic or Hazardous Material

Handling Chemicals

Radiology labs must follow Occupational Safety and Health Administration (OSHA) policies to protect staff from exposure to hazardous materials. The best practice is to eliminate any exposure if at all possible. However, in certain situations employees will need to handle chemicals. If there are alternative chemicals that are deemed safer, they should be utilized instead. It is imperative that the staff is trained in proper procedures and know how to use engineering controls. These controls include lab equipment that supplies adequate ventilation and isolating the chemicals from other areas of the building. Administrative protocols should also be implemented so that staff is rotated through tasks and shifts to limit their exposure to toxic chemicals. Personal protective equipment (PPE) should also be supplied to all staff so they can protect themselves from exposure to hazardous materials. PPE includes gowns, gloves, face shields, and eye protection. Respirators may also be necessary, and in other cases radiation badges should be provided.

Handling Chemotherapy Materials

Staff who handle chemotherapy materials must have the proper training to prevent exposure to themselves, coworkers, families, pets, and patients that they will come into contact with. Prepping for chemotherapy administration should be performed in a dedicated lab that is considered to be a low-traffic workspace. It should be easy to maintain cleanliness in this area. Staff that is in charge of inventory and/or receiving chemotherapy medications must be aware that the external surfaces of packaging may be contaminated. Proper personal protective equipment (PPE) must be used during the prep, administration, and cleanup of chemo agents. If ventilation hoods are not available, respirators should be used. Special biologic safety cabinets should be utilized when available so that chemotherapy drugs can be stored separately from drugs not used for cancer patients. Pill counters should be used and stored with cancer medications so that routine meds are not cross-contaminated. Employees who are pregnant, nursing, or planning to become pregnant should avoid handling these materials.

OSHA and SDS

OSHA stands for Occupational Safety and Health Administration. It is an organization designed to assure the safety and health of workers by setting and enforcing standards; providing training, outreach, and education; establishing partnerships; and encouraging continual improvement in workplace safety and health.

SDS (formerly MSDS) stands for Safety Data Sheets. These sheets are the result of the "Right to Know" Law also known as the OSHA's HazCom Standard. This law requires chemical manufacturers to supply SDS sheets on any products that have a hazardous warning label. These sheets contain information on precautionary as well as emergency information about the product.

Pharmacology

Medication Reconciliation

Medication reconciliation is an important step while obtaining a patient's history. It provides important data to clinicians about the current medications (prescription and over the counter), reasons for taking the drugs, dosage, and how often the medication is taken. Medication reconciliation is a safety measure to prevent any harm to patients but can be a difficult task as, often, patients are not able to give a complete history (unless they bring in the packages for all of their medications) and may see more than one provider. Technologists should ask patients about any medications that they are taking to make sure that there aren't any contraindications when injections or oral contrast media is to be used. Often, patients may be confused as to why they take a certain medication, so technologists should become familiar with medications to provide additional insight regarding diseases or disorders the patient may have.

Premedication

Medical professionals should realize that premedicating patients who have had prior allergic reactions to contrast used in the radiology department does not guarantee that an adverse reaction will not take place again. When premedicating a patient is deemed necessary, the preferred route tends to be by mouth. Oral prednisone has been found to be a favorable method due to cost-effectiveness and easy accessibility. Patients will typically start taking prednisone 13, 7, and 1 hour prior to the procedure. Some patients may also be given Benadryl an hour prior to the exam. If a patient is unable to take the medication orally, then medication will be administered by an IV of Solu-Medrol® several hours prior to the time of injection (typically starting 5 hours before). Every radiology department will have specific protocols that they suggest, so technologists should always be sure to check with the radiologist if any questions arise. All patients should be aware of the risks associated with the use of contrast media.

Contraindications to Watch for Regarding a Patient's History

Technologists should check the patient's medical record as well as ask the patient prior to an injection about any prior contrast reaction or if they have allergies. Individuals who have had a prior reaction are five times more likely to react to the same contrast agent. Patients with other allergies are two to three times more likely to react to the contrast medium. Other contraindications for radiology exams that utilize contrast are renal disease, asthma, and heart disease. It is important to check labs pertaining to kidney function. Patients who display anxiety during the exam are more likely to have mild contrast reactions, so it is important to explain the procedure and answer any questions the patient may have to put them at ease. Technologists should also consider the age of a patient before administering contrast media. Although the elderly are more prone to renal and heart disease, they typically react to contrast media less than patients who are middle age.

Scheduling and Screening Processes

Most medical facilities have employees who coordinate the scheduling of the test and the availability of the practitioner who will be performing the screening. An initial low-dose test is performed to test the patient for the baseline screening 18, and the patient is informed about the radiation dose, carcinogenic effects, and other specific information related to the benefits and risks of testing. Some facilities provide this information in a brochure with the consent form that must be completed before testing. Contact information and details about any indications or contraindications are obtained by the coordinator during the scheduling interview before administration of the test. If necessary, follow-up appointments or repeated screenings can also be scheduled.

Scheduling Sequence of Multiple Procedures

Sometimes a physician orders multiple procedures. It is important that the radiographer conducts these procedures in the correct order so that the contrast media used to enhance the image does not interfere with subsequent procedures. It is important that a radiographer is aware of how contras media can obscure an image. To minimize interference between procedures, some procedures should be conducted in a specific order. The following is the order in which certain procedures should be conducted:

1. Intravenous pyelogram (IVP)
2. Gallbladder study (GB)
3. Barium enema (BE)
4. Upper Gastrointestinal study (UGI)

IVP and BE studies and GB and UGI studies can be conducted on the same day.

Materials Needed for Inserting an IV Line

For some CT examinations, an IV line must be inserted before testing so that the contrast agent can be administered. Before the test begins, the practitioner should gather the proper materials for administering the IV. Those materials include absorbent disposable sheets or towels; alcohol wipes for preparing the arm; a tourniquet; angiocatheter or butterfly needles; IV tubing, such as Smart Set; a 30-cc syringe filled with 30 cc of normal saline; several pieces of gauze cut into 4-in or 2-in squares; and 4 pieces of tape precut into 4-in (10-cm) strips and conveniently located at the table or stretcher. Rubber gloves should be worn at all times.

Administration of IV and Oral Contrast Materials

Practitioners may choose to administer contrast materials intravenously as a bolus injection or as a continuous infusion. IV administration is acceptable for ionic or nonionic contrast agents. Butterfly needles are preferable for direct IV injections because they allow the practitioner to change large syringes more easily. For an angiocatheter IV, a 20- or 22-gauge needle should be used, and the practitioner should be experienced enough to know how much force is necessary to slide the plastic catheter over the metal stylet.

Oral contrast agents depict different portions of the organ or tissues being studied, because low concentrations of paramagnetic dye can cause a reduction in T1 relaxation time, whereas high concentrations can cause T2 shortening similar to that seen with superparamagnetic iron oxide in decreasing the signal. Buffering is necessary for oral contrast because the Gd-DTPA chelates are unstable at low pH levels in the stomach.

Preparation of Patient for IV Injection

The practitioner should introduce himself or herself to the patient before preparing the IV injection. The practitioner should ask whether the patient has previously experienced an IV injection and whether the patient would like to discuss any complications or concerns. The practitioner may educate the patient at this time about what will be done and about the purpose for the IV in relation to the CT scan. Patients who are familiar with the process involved in placing an IV may have a preferred location, such as the outer arm or hand. The patient can direct the practitioner to this area, although the antecubital fossa should be considered the default location because of the large, easily accessible antecubital vein.

Preparation of IV Tubing

Practitioners can attach to the intravenous tubing both a syringe for administering the contrast agent and a syringe for administering the saline flush. The Smart Set complements dynamic contrast injections for various tests and has one-way valves that allow the practitioner to alternate between the contrast injection and the saline flush, thereby allowing a continuous bolus with no gaps. With experience, the practitioner can also determine whether the patient has experienced any negative reactions to the injection. The practitioner should verify that no large air bubbles exist in the saline line when filling the tubing. Any off-the-shelf IV tubing should be clamped so that the saline does not drip. Most Smart Set devices have valves that are usually in a closed position.

Venipuncture

Several important factors must be considered during the performance of venipuncture, or surgical puncture of a vein, for drawing blood or administering intravenous medication. The common veins used for such administration should be located before venipuncture is performed, and all necessary equipment and departmental pharmaceuticals should be readily available. These pharmaceuticals may include iodine-based contrast material, such as ionic and nonionic contrast dyes; high osmolar and low osmolar contrast agents, which are associated with adverse effects, precautions, dose requirements, varying susceptibility of body parts to the contrast, and peak opacification time; and sedation agents, which are associated with adverse effects, precautions, and dose requirements. The appropriate site must be selected and prepared for venipuncture, and the practitioner must insert and remove the needle correctly.

Best Vein for Venipuncture Between Cubital, Basilica, and Cephalic Veins

First choice would be the median cubital due to its large size, and it usually doesn't bruise severely. Next choice would be the cephalic vein since it does not roll as easily as other veins. A last resort vein would be the basilica vein because it rolls easily and is positioned so that the brachial artery and a major nerve are at risk for puncture if used. Ankle and foot veins should only be punctured at the discretion of a physician and should only be used when no other veins are appropriate. Poor circulation and clotting factors may affect results of tests and cause puncture wounds that may not readily heal.

Blood Vessels

Types

The following are types of blood vessels:

- Arteries - blood vessels that carry blood away from the heart to the body, does not have valves
- Veins - blood vessels that carry the blood from the body back to the heart, has valves
- Capillaries – one cell thick blood vessels between arteries and veins that distribute oxygen-rich blood to the body
- Venules- the smallest veins
- Arterioles- the smallest arteries.

Layers

The wall of an artery consists of three (3) distinct layers of tunics:

- Tunica intima – Composed of simple, squamous epithelium called endothelium. Rests on a connective tissue membrane that is rich in elastic and collagenous fibers.
- Tunica media – Makes up the bulk of the arterial wall. Includes smooth muscle fibers, which encircle the tube, and a thick layer of elastic connective tissue.
- Tunica adventitia – Consists chiefly of connective tissue with irregularly arranged elastic and collagenous fibers. This layer attaches the artery to the surrounding tissues. Also contains minute vessels (vasa vasorum--vessels of vessels) that give rise to capillaries and provide blood to the more external cells of the artery wall.

Smooth muscles in the walls of arteries and arterioles are innervated by the sympathetic branches of the autonomic nervous system.

The Tunica media and the Tunica adventitia is much thicker in arteries.

Great Saphenous, Popliteal, Femoral, and Lesser Saphenous Veins

The great saphenous vein runs the entire length of the lower extremity and is the longest vein in the body. The Popliteal vein runs deep behind the knee. The femoral vein runs deep in the upper part of the leg. The lesser saphenous vein runs lateral to the ankle, up the leg and deep behind the knee.

Arteries of the Upper Limb

The following are arteries of the upper limb:

- Internal thoracic - Descends posteriorly to the clavicle's sternal end and enters the thorax.
- Thyrocervical trunk - A short trunk that ascends and gives off four different branches, including the transverse and ascending cervical, and suprascapular.
- Suprascapular - Travels inferolaterally, follows the clavicle in a parallel manner, then goes posteriorly to the scapula.
- Subscapular - Descends along subscapularis muscle's lateral border to the inferior angle of the scapula.
- Thoracodorsal - Accompanies the nerve of the same name to latissimus dorsi muscle
- Deep Brachial - Accompanies the radial nerve as they pass through the humeral radial groove, then it anastomoses around the elbow joint.
- Ulnar Collateral - Anastomoses around the elbow joint.

Gauge of Needle and Needle Selection

The gauge of a needle is a number that is inversely correlates to the diameter of the internal space of the needle for example the larger the needle the smaller the internal space of the needle and the smaller the number the larger the internal space of the needle. Since color-coding varies between manufactures, be careful of using this method to determine the gauge of a needle. When selecting a needle for venipuncture, there are several factors to consider which include the type of procedure, the condition and size of the patient's vein, and the equipment being used. The length of the needle used is determined by the depth of the vein. Keep in mind that the smaller the gauge the larger the bore. The 21-gauge needle is the standard needle used for routine venipuncture.

Needle Safety Devices

Needle safety devices protect the needle user's hand by having it remain behind the needle during use and by providing a barrier between the user's hand and the needle after use. Also, the needle safety devices are operable with using a one-handed technique and provide a permanent barrier around the contaminated needle.

Proper Venipuncture Technique for Radiography Setting

The injection of contrast media may be necessary for exams performed in the radiology department. The preferred location for exams that are performed on adults and utilize a power injection is the antecubital vein. If these vessels are too deep or tend to roll too much, the forearm also offers a suitable location. Regardless of the method of injection (by hand or power injector), a vein must be properly accessed by the following steps: gather the necessary supplies, choose the best vein, decide on the proper gauge of the catheter, apply tourniquet roughly 2 inches proximal to the site, cleanse the area with an alcohol wipe, insert the catheter and look for flashback as the needle enters the vein, remove the needle using the safety engineer so that a needle stick is prevented prior to dropping it into a sharps container, and secure the catheter with tape so the IV stays in place. It is advisable to check the IV with saline prior to injecting the contrast media.

Contrast Media

Contrast media is used in radiography to increase the contrast of certain tissues and anatomy that do not naturally have adequate contrast on the radiographic image. It is necessary, for example, when imaging the abdominal area because all of the organs in this area have similar densities, and therefore little natural contrast. The contrast agents used in radiography are radiopaque (positive) or radiolucent (negative). Iodinated agents and barium sulfate suspensions are the two types of radiopaque contrast agents used. Gases, such as carbon dioxide and air, are radiolucent agents. Radiopaque agents provide contrast for structures while radiolucent agents provide contrast for spaces. For this reason, the two types of contrast agents are often used together.

Safety Issues, Alternatives, and Preferences

Contrast materials are used during radiography, ultrasonography, nuclear imaging, and magnetic resonance imaging so that practitioners can view the target organ and surrounding tissue without performing open surgery and can thereby analyze the current condition of the patient's internal organs. Current research on contrast materials focuses either on developing new types of agents, thereby allowing easier and safer diagnosis, or on modifying current agents to reduce their impact on health care expenses. Debate has centered on comparing the cost and benefits of available contrast materials with their relative toxicity. Researchers have rapidly developed technological improvements, and the combination of dynamic changes in market behavior and the high cost of imaging technology in health care expenses has initiated much discussion about the types of contrast materials and their relative benefits for patients.

Contrast Media Dose Calculation

Many exams that are performed in the radiology department require the use of contrast media, whether it is in the form of barium sulfate that will be ingested or intravenous contrast. Every facility will have departmental policies and protocols in place for specific exams regarding how much contrast should be used. However, radiologic technologists must also consider the age, weight, and physical condition of each patient and should look at the patient history and thoroughly screen the patient before the administration of any contrast agent. Many departments have multiple radiologists, so it is also important to discern which radiologist will be reading the study so that his or her protocols are followed. Contrast media dosage is not the same for every exam because the protocol varies due to the concentration of iodine that is used, the volume, and how quickly the bolus is injected. Dose limits for the injection of IV contrast in pediatric patients will vary, but some facilities calculate the amount of contrast as 2 mL/kg of body weight.

Effect on Image Resolution

Practitioners anticipate that the effects of contrast material will be noticeable during analysis because the contrast material augments the contrast resolution by an increased photoelectric effect. Any discernable contrast improvement can be directly correlated to the degree of iodine concentration in the contrast dye because the atomic number of iodine is 53 (Z:53). Peak iodine blood concentration is observed in patients within 2 minutes after the intravenous (IV) injection. At this point, the biologic half-life of the iodinated contrast material in the vascular compartment is approximately 20 minutes. The iodinated contrast material is then transferred from the vascular compartment to the extravascular compartment within 10 minutes so that the equilibrium is followed by a measured decrease in both compartments. Although severely impaired renal function results in poor contrast resolution and prolonged plasma levels, renal accumulation occurs within 1 minute, and the maximum contrast is evident within 5 to 15 minutes.

Excretion

Although the expected biologic half-life of contrast materials ranges from 10 to 90 minutes, practitioners should inform patients that 90% of the contrast material will be excreted within 24 hours of injection and that the peak urine concentration of the dye will occur within 2 hours of administration. The main excretion route for any contrast material is through the kidneys, although the body can excrete the dye through the liver. Thus, patients with poor renal function are more likely to excrete the dye through the small intestine or the gallbladder. Excretions that occur during nursing of infants do not change the contrast material.

Barium Sulfate

As a positive diamagnetic contrast agent, barium sulfate causes a loss of signal in the bowel because of 1) the predilection of barium to replace the water protons and 2) the magnetic capacity attributed to the barium particles. The results of current testing of conventional barium sulfate suspension at 60% wt/wt are encouraging. Loss of signal is greater in higher concentrations of the barium sulfate contrast agent with 170% to 220% wt/vl suspensions than in the original barium suspension. Although the loss of signal in the barium sulfate suspensions is not comparable to the loss of signal in superparamagnetic iron oxide agents, the barium suspensions are more readily available for practitioners and are usually less expensive than other contrast agents.

Anticoagulation in Ionic and Nonionic Contrast Material

Studies have shown that blood clot formation occurs in angiographic syringes that contain nonionic contrast material. When these agents interact and coagulate blood, practitioners should remember that low osmolar nonionic contrast media exert less of an anticoagulant effect than ionic contrast media do, because the ionic contrast media interact with the hemostatic system on different levels and inhibit fibrin monomer polymerization by binding with and inactivating the protein necessary for coagulation. Ionic contrast media can also hinder the ability of thrombin to activate platelets. Nonionic agents do not affect the system in this manner. Other studies suggest that the use of ionic contrast media may be linked to reduce thrombus formation, with fewer closures of acute vessels and marked reduction in platelet deposits and thrombi during angioplasty procedures.

Air

Air can also be used as a contrast agent in certain studies, although the use of air is not as common as the use of a liquid dye. During a study aimed at comparing air and liquid as contrast agents in the diagnosis and reduction of intussusception, or at drawing a length of intestine into an adjacent portion to produce obstruction, practitioners discovered that air enemas could be considered effective contrast agents for more than half of the patients included in the study. These results show that air is as effective a contrast agent as liquid contrast material. When air was used for fluoroscopic or x-ray viewing of opaque internal structures, the imaging times were shorter when practitioners had experience with using air as a contrast agent. Air is not always the preferred method, however, and its use should be thoroughly studied before it is implemented.

Water-Soluble Contrast Agents

Water-soluble contrast agents may be preferable in studies of certain organs, such as the small bowel. Although ionic contrast agents are usually used in comparable studies, nonionic agents can be considered viable alternatives in particular circumstances when barium sulfate is contraindicated. Any inclusion of a water-soluble contrast agent should be properly documented, although such decisions should be made after radiographic quality and other clinical findings have been studied. A diagnosis of obstruction may be confirmed by radiologic findings. Practitioners should identify any fistulae or abnormal passageways from hollow organs to other hollow organs or to the surface of the skin, any obstructions in patients who have been treated with laparotomy, and any problems in the surgical section of the abdominal wall, as these conditions have not been noted in patients with negative results from previous examinations with contrast. Most patients can tolerate nonionic water-soluble follow-through examinations, which provide accurate diagnoses of any obstruction or fistula.

Correlation with Patient Condition for Standard Exams

Exams of the gastrointestinal (GI) tract require barium to visualize the structures well. However, if a perforated bowel, abscess, or fistula is suspected, it is assumed the patient will have surgery, and barium should not be used. In these situations, or if it is a study that is done prior to an endoscopy exam, a water-soluble iodine oral contrast will be used instead. Studies have shown that contrast is passed into the fetus via the placenta, but it has been deemed safe for mothers who are breast-feeding to continue to do so after iodinated or gadolinium contrast studies. If these patients do not feel comfortable with these guidelines, it is suggested that they pump and discard breast milk for 24 hours after the exam and then continue nursing as usual. It is considered safe for patients on dialysis to receive a reasonable dose of contrast media as their kidneys are no longer working and cannot cause any further damage. However, if a dialysis patient receives a large volume of contrast and has a history of cardiac risk factors, he or she may need to undergo dialysis following the contrast exam.

Impact of Patient Age and Weight

Technologists must consider the weight of the patient when contrast is requested for an exam. The patient's weight must be considered for exams that require contrast injections or oral contrast as blood volume may be increased with contrast that has a higher osmolality. Pediatric and elderly patients that have a history of cardiac or renal complications may be more susceptible to pulmonary edema or even cardiac failure due to the shift of fluid from soft tissue into the circulatory system after an injection. Studies have shown that the populations that have fewer reactions to contrast are the elderly and pediatric patients (including neonates and infants). Men also have fewer reactions when compared to female patients. Some radiology protocols require the same dose for all patients, whereas other labs base the dosage on lean body weight. This actually reduces the amount of contrast in patients who are heavier as the dose is not calculated on total body weight.

Power Injection vs. Manual Injection

Either power injection or manual injection can be used to administer intravenous contrast material, although power injection provides uniformity of enhancement and allows the practitioner to verify the precise timing of the delivery of contrast materials. Power injection is most often used with intravenous catheters so that the injection site can be closely monitored during the initial injection and the risk of extravasation can be minimized. The flow rate should be set so that the entire amount of contrast material can be delivered over a period determined to be equal to or slightly less than that required for CT acquisition. Manual injection is preferred when intravenous access is achieved through a catheter located in the dorsum of the hand or wrist. If the catheter is properly positioned and well-functioning, the complications associated with both methods of injection are similar.

Sterile Solutions in Bulk

Single-use, prepackaged products can be replaced with bulk solutions in certain situations. Practitioners cannot sterilize the antiseptic solutions used to prepare the patient's arm, but these solutions can be purchased and prepared in bulk and will last for several months with proper handling. Certain solutions contain additives such as alcohol or iodophor compound that can prevent the growth of organisms. Bulk products requiring dilution should be handled in small batches at a time. Bottles of iodine solutions purchased in bulk should be tightly sealed or capped when not being used in venipuncture preparation, because alcohol evaporates over time. This potential evaporation could increase the concentration of iodine, thereby resulting in skin irritation.

Power and Manual Injections for Pediatric Patients

Power and manual injections can be used almost interchangeably for most patients, although the appropriateness of power injection involving a 24-gauge peripheral catheter has not been well established for infants and children. With proper intravascular positioning of the access, power injection can be safe for pediatric patients as long as the return of blood and the delivery of saline flush or cleansing are unimpeded. With contrast material delivered at 1.0 mL/sec, many medical facilities are seeing improvements in power injections for pediatric populations when the injection occurs through central venous access if peripheral access is unavailable.

Contrast Media Injection Safety

The technologist performing the injection should communicate to the patient why it is a necessary portion of the exam. Prior to starting an IV, the technologist should properly screen the patient per the departmental protocol for any prior contrast reaction. If labs were required, it is important that the technologist reviews them as well. The correct gauge must be chosen for the site and bolus requirements, and once it is in place, a saline check should be performed. The power injector must be properly loaded to eliminate any chance of injecting air into the patient's IV. Once everything is satisfactory, before leaving the room, the technologist should monitor the injection site for the first 15 seconds by feeling the area to make sure that extravasation has not taken place. Once the exam is finished, the technologist should do a final evaluation pertaining to how the patient is feeling before removing the access site in case medication needs to be administered for any reaction.

Single- and Dual-Head Power Injectors

Power injectors are specialized equipment used for the injection of a bolus of contrast material. These tools offer consistent and rapid capabilities depending on the necessary applications required by the exam protocol and patient's health status. Power injectors may be used during single or multiphase exam protocols as timing delays can be programmed into the equipment. Single head power injectors are automatic injectors that allow technologists to inject radiographic contrast via an angiocatheter. Dual head power injectors include an additional head containing saline that is useful to flush after the contrast injection. This not only flushes the contrast out of the patient's system more readily, but for some exams it will help alleviate some of the artifact caused by a large bolus of contrast. Technologists must take caution when using a power injector as the possibility of extravasation is higher and could create serious damage to the tissue.

Automatic Injection

Automatic injection methods include the bolus method, in which the solution is automatically provided over a short period of time; the gravity infusion method, in which the bag of solution is connected to the tubing and needle and is administered with a timer; and the infusion pump method, in which an electronic control determines the rate and volume of the solution being injected. Automatic injection techniques are programmed for single-phase injection or multi-phase injection as determined by the power of the energy being released. The flow rate for those injections is determined by the density of the solution, the amount of time needed to administer the entire solution, and the comparable amount of time required to complete the CT scan.

Contraindications for Contrast Media Use

Radiopaque contrast agents are used to provide structural contrast in parts of the anatomy with similar densities, and so little radiographic contrast. Barium sulfate suspensions are used when imaging the GI (gastrointestinal) tract. Its use is contraindicated, however, if there is a suspected tear or ulcer because barium could escape into the peritoneal cavity. It is also contraindicated for use with NG (nasogastric) tubing or any form of ostomy. In these cases, water-soluble iodinated contrast agents are recommended. Iodinated contrast agents can be either ionic or nonionic. Nonionic agents are recommended for use in children, the elderly, patients with renal disease, and those with allergies (particularly allergic reaction to contrast media). Side effects (nausea, vomiting, and cardiovascular complications) and allergic reactions are less likely with nonionic agents. They are, however, considerably more expensive than ionic contrast agents.

Local Effects of Contrast Media Reactions

Contrast media is often used in the radiology department, especially during computed tomography (CT) procedures. Extravasation with power injections may result in a greater quantity of fluid that has escaped versus a hand injection, but it may occur with either method. Although some patients cannot feel the contrast escaping into the nearby tissue, others complain of a burning, full sensation. In addition to pain at the injection site, swelling and redness are other symptoms to look for. Technologists should immediately check the site (and quickly discontinued if necessary) if a patient communicates that it is painful. Iodinated contrast has been shown to damage surrounding tissue more than non-iodinated contrast, but extravasation must be properly documented. The radiologist should also be notified immediately to assess the patient, and even if the patient is allowed to leave, he or she should be told to monitor the area for the next 24 to 48 hours. A radiologist may feel that a surgical consult may be necessary in cases of extreme extravasation.

Potential Physical Responses of Patient to Medication Administered During CT

The contrast dye administered to facilitate CT scanning may cause flushing, itching, rash, rapid heart rate, drop in blood pressure, respiratory distress, or hives in some patients as much as 6 hours after the procedure. The contrast material may cause acute kidney failure in some patients, although the risk of this occurrence is higher for patients with certain pre-existing conditions. Diabetic patients may require an adjustment in medication or fluid intake so that any potential problems can be minimized during and after the procedure. All patients should drink plenty of fluids after the procedure to flush out the contrast dye. Although newer types of contrast agents are being developed to minimize possible allergic reactions, each patient should discuss any potential changes in medication before testing.

Allergic and Adverse Reactions to Contrast Agents

Not all patients respond to contrast agents in the same way or even in safe ways. Patients may have an adverse reaction to the nonionic iodine used during contrast-enhanced CT. Under these circumstances, practitioners should verify that the patient's vital signs are carefully monitored. For some patients, the response to contrast agents involves a negative change in the pulse rate, in the systolic and diastolic arterial blood pressure, and in the arterial blood oxygen saturation level. Physical responses can be minor, intermediate, or severe. Nausea and pharyngeal discomfort are the most common symptoms reported by patients who experience negative reactions, although some patients have also exhibited prolonged hypotension, transient hypotension or hypertension, facial edema, and urticaria defined by raised patches of skin or mucous membranes and serious itching, sometimes with no obvious clinical symptoms. Before the introduction of dye, practitioners should determine whether the patient has any medication allergies; during the procedure, practitioners should monitor the patient's vital signs closely.

Emergency Medications

Radiologic technologists should carefully monitor all patients for any change in their vital signs and for any indications of contrast reactions. Employees should know the location of basic medical supplies such as a blood pressure cuff, pulse oximeter, stethoscope, and crash cart. Medications such as Benadryl, epinephrine, albuterol, and atropine should be on hand in case it is necessary to administer them. The crash cart must also be available in case the patient needs to be resuscitated. Technologists should always make sure the supplies on the crash cart are stocked and that the medications are not expired. Routine checks should also be performed in the exam rooms to make sure the oxygen and suction are working properly.

Safety

Principles of Radiation Physics

Ionizing Radiation

The four types of ionizing radiation are x-rays, gamma rays, alpha particles, and beta particles. The type of shield necessary for each type of radiation depends on its energy level. X-rays and gamma rays are similar in that they both can pass through the human body and require a dense material, such as lead, to provide adequate shielding. Alpha particles can be absorbed by a person's skin and an adequate shield would be a simple piece of paper. Beta particles pass through the skin, but not through the body. An appropriate shield for beta particles is a sheet of aluminum 1/25" thick.

X-Ray Beam

Electrons are produced within the x-ray tube by the heating of a cathode filament. When electricity is applied, the electrons are forced to the anode. The focal point of this reaction is a tungsten target. The positive charge of the tungsten nucleus acts as a strong attractor for the electrons. The electrons, which are moving at a high speed, are effectively stopped in their tracks by the strong attraction. This sharp deceleration causes the conversion of the kinetic energy contained within the electrons into highly energized, highly penetrating electromagnetic radiations. These are x-ray photons.

Rectification

Rectification is the process that takes alternating current (AC) and converts it into direct current (DC). Transformers, which are used in x-ray circuitry, require AC to operate. Direct current, however, is needed in the x-ray tube for the production of x-rays. The current, therefore, must be rectified before it reaches the tube. Single-phase rectification does the job of changing AC to DC, but because the there is still a voltage drop, this produces x-rays of various energies. In the interest of minimizing unnecessary exposure to ionizing radiation, it is best to use a beam with a uniform energy. This way the patient absorbs less radiation. The way to address this is with three-phase rectification. In this rectification process, three AC waveforms are superimposed on each other with a slight shift in position. The result is a nearly constant waveform (mono-energetic) with little voltage drop.

Construction of X-Ray Tube

There are three major components of the x-ray tube: the cathode, which is the negative pole; the anode, which is the positive pole; and the glass envelope. The cathode consists of a tungsten filament and focusing cup. It is connected to both the high-voltage and filament circuit of the x-ray circuit. The anode contains the target for x-ray production and can be either stationary or rotating. It is connected to the high-voltage portion of the x-ray circuit. The glass envelope encases both the cathode and anode and provides the vacuum necessary to allow the unobstructed movement of electrons from cathode to anode. The area around the glass envelope is filled with oil, which helps to improve the overall thermal conductivity of the tube.

Role of Generators and Induction Motors in X-Ray Production

A generator takes mechanical energy and turns it into electrical energy, and a motor takes electrical energy and turns it into mechanical energy. Although they perform opposite functions, both are necessary elements in x-ray production. The anode, where the actual production of x-rays occurs, is a generator that takes the kinetic energy of fast-moving electrons and converts it into x-rays. To increase the efficiency of x-ray production, the anode in most x-ray units today is a rotating anode. A motor is necessary to drive the movement of the anode, allowing it to accept electrons at very high speeds without damage due to the production of heat.

Electron Source for X-Ray Production

A negatively charged electron cloud is formed within the focusing cup when heat is applied to the filament in the cathode (negative pole) of the x-ray tube. This electron cloud is called a space charge and is the source of electrons for x-ray production. The process of applying heat to release a charge is called thermionic emission (or boiling off of electrons) and occurs when the heat applied to metal is great enough that it breaks the electrostatic forces holding electrons to the surface. The filament of the cathode is made of tungsten. Tungsten is used because it has a high enough melting point (3410 degrees C) to withstand the amount of heat needed to produce ionizing radiation without melting or becoming damaged. Many x-ray tubes have both a large and small filament. The smaller the filament, the fewer electrons are produced, thus limiting the size of the x-ray beam.

Tungsten

Tungsten is used for the target material in the x-ray tube for several reasons. It has a high enough melting point (3410 degrees C) to withstand the amount of heat needed to produce ionizing radiation without melting or becoming damaged. The thermal conductivity of the metal allows for better heat dissipation. Finally, because it has a high atomic number (74), it increases the production of x-rays. This means that the positively charged nuclease has the ability to attract the fast-moving electrons produced at the cathode end of the tube and convert the kinetic energy to x-rays.

Bremsstrahlung Radiation

Bremsstrahlung radiation (also called brems or breaking radiation) is the radiation that makes up most of the x-ray beam and can occur at any energy level. In this type of radiation, an electron interacts with the nucleus. There is no collision in the interaction, just a strong attraction between positive (the nucleus) and negative (the electron) charges. The force of the attraction between electron and nucleus is so strong that nearly all of the energy of the electron is released from the atom in the form of x-radiation. The electron, which has just lost its energy, floats away from the nucleus.

Electron Sources

There are three basic elements required to generate an x-ray: the electron source, mechanism of acceleration, and interaction target. Matter consists of atoms, which have electrons that orbit about the nucleus of the atom in orbital shells. To obtain electrons, the electrons must be liberated from the respective orbital shell. The method to liberate electrons is straightforward. By putting a current through a piece of wire, the resistance in the wire will cause the wire to generate heat. The generation of heat by the wire serves to excite the electrons, which, in turn, causes the electrons to leave the wire to use the energy that was generated by the heat of the current.

Characteristic Radiation

Characteristic radiation is an x-ray interaction that relates to (or is characteristic of) the target of the radiation. It is similar to photoelectric interactions in that the photons interact with inner shell electrons, causing the outer shell electrons to shed energy and move in closer to the nucleus. The target atom, however, has a high atomic number (and thus high binding energy of electrons) and so this interaction requires radiation of a high energy level. Thus, the radiation is characteristic of the atomic number and binding energy of the target (hence the name).

Frequency and Wavelength of Photon Energy

Photons are the "packets" of energy that make up the electromagnetic spectrum. All electromagnetic radiations have photons that have a wave-like motion. This is a characteristic that is the same across all types of radiation, regardless of the amount of energy. What is different is the amount of energy contained within a particular type of radiation. And this is dictated by the wavelength and frequency of the photons. Wavelength describes the distance between the crests of consecutive waves. Frequency refers to the number of waves in a given time (cycles per second), in other words, how frequently the photon rises and falls as it travels along. Wavelength and frequency are inversely proportional: as the distance between crests of the wave shorten (wavelength decreases), more cycles can occur each second (frequency increases). Photons with a higher frequency have more energy and a greater penetrating power.

Exposure Factors in Quantity and Quality of X-Ray Beam

When x-ray photons pass through living tissue, they leave behind energy that has the potential to cause chemical or biological changes. To minimize the potential damage, the quality and quantity of radiation is adjusted. There are two exposure factors that are manipulated to produce an x-ray beam: mAs and kVp. The quantity of the x-ray beam is dependent on the mAs, which is a measurement of the quantity of photons over time produced by the x-ray equipment. The quality of the beam is dependent on the kVp, which is a measurement of the penetrating ability of the beam. Ideally, a patient should be exposed to the least amount of radiation yet still get the best possible picture. A lower mAs setting produces fewer photons, and so lessens the number of photons a patient is exposed to and a higher kVp setting produces a high quality beam that penetrates the patient, as opposed to being absorbed by the patient.

Primary and Remnant Radiation

Primary radiation is a term used in medical applications of radiation and refers to the radiation that leaves the tube port of the x-ray or CT equipment, before it reaches the patient. Remnant radiation refers to the radiation that exits the patient's body during a medical application and results in the formation of an image on the image receptor. The patient's body absorbs a certain amount of radiation as it passes through, attenuating the amount of energy left to make an image. It is sometimes referred to as exit or image-forming radiation. Remnant radiation is calculated as the primary radiation minus the image forming radiation.

Inverse Square Law

The Inverse Square Law is a mathematical description of what happens to the intensity of exposure as an individual moves further from a source of radiation. The intensity of radiation is inversely proportional to the distance squared. For every foot that a person moves away from a source of radiation, the intensity is reduced by the amount of change in distance squared. If a person is exposed to 100mr/hr of radiation at a distance of 4 feet, and they move to a distance 8 feet from the radiation source, the distance is effectually twice as far away, meaning the radiation will be a quarter as intense, or 25mr/hr. Similarly, if the same person were to move to a distance of 2 feet from the radiation source, the intensity would be quadrupled to be 400mr/hr of radiation. This illustrates how greatly the distance from the source of radiation affects the mount of exposure. Thus, distance from the source of radiation is a simple but effective way to minimize occupational exposure.

Magnetism

Magnetism is the force that either attracts or repels materials as a result of the force field that is created by the movement of charged particles. There are three types of magnets. One is a natural magnet such as lodestone, a naturally magnetic rock found in the earth. The second are artificial permanent magnets. These manmade steel magnets never lose their charge. Electromagnets are the third type of magnet. They are also artificial, but their magnetism is temporary. The laws of magnets state that every magnet has two poles, referred to as north and south poles; like poles repel each other, unlike poles attract each other; and the force of the magnetic field decreases by the square of the distance between poles (inverse square law).

Ionizing Radiation

Radiation is a form of energy that is a part of the electromagnetic spectrum and is made up of units of energy called "photons." Photons have no mass or weight. They travel in a wave motion, and wavelength is what differentiates the different types of electromagnetic radiations. Electromagnetic radiations with long wavelengths are low-energy radiations with the ability to travel great distances (i.e. radio waves) but have little penetrating power. Ionizing radiations, on the other hand, have a shorter wavelength, a higher frequency, and a greater penetrating power. Ionizing radiation has enough power to displace electrons in an atom's orbit. This leaves the atom charged (or ionized). If the ionized atom is in a living system, it can result in biological or chemical changes.

Properties of X-Ray Photons

The basic properties of x-ray photons are as follows:

- Move in a wave-like motion
- Travel in a straight line at the speed of light (3 EE 8 m/sc)
- Cannot be detected by the senses and have no charge
- Highly energized and have the ability to ionize air
- Because of their high frequency, they have the ability to penetrate all matter
- Penetrating effect can result in chemical and biological changes in an organism
- Have a photographic effect on film
- Cause certain phosphors to fluoresce
- Can be directed at a target, but cannot be focused

Internal Conversion

Internal conversion is also referred to as electronic conversion. This takes place after a gamma ray is released by a nucleus in an excited state. The gamma emission comes into contact with a K shell electron. The electron is ejected from the K shell and interacts with the gamma, which leaves a vacant space where the electron was located. The gamma disappears as it is assimilated by the electron. As the atom adjusts to compensate for the void in the K shell, an electron from the L shell will replace the missing electron, and an electron is emitted. Gamma decay is an example like all internal conversions in which the atomic number does not change. In this case there won't be a conversion of one element to another.

Scatter Radiation

Once x-ray beams interact with matter, such as tissues, organs, protective clothing, and each other, those beams change direction. Classic scattering is the changing of the direction of the x-ray beams without a subsequent loss of energy; it is defined as coherent, Rayleigh, or Thompson scattering. Compton scattering is the ionization and x-ray scattering that result from the interaction between the x-ray and a loosely bound outer-shell electron, also known as a Compton electron, which is emitted from the outer shell of the atom in response to x-ray scattering. Scatter radiation can reduce contrast and produce less contrast resolution in the image, whereas larger prepatient and postpatient collimation produces more scatter radiation.

Photodisintegration Interactions of X-Radiation

Photodisintegration interactions of x-radiation are extremely high-energy interactions that occur at energy levels of 10 megaelectron volts (MeV) and higher. In these interactions, a photon (incident photon) has enough energy to enter an atom and interact with its nucleus, resulting in the ejection of a neutron or nuclear fragment that is very fast, highly penetrating and highly ionizing. Particles created from these types of interactions will continue to interact with other atoms until all of the radiation is absorbed. Because of the high energy levels used, this type of interaction can be found in radiation therapy (not diagnostic radiography).

Compton Interactions of X-Radiation

The Compton interactions of x-radiation are high-energy interactions, occurring at energy levels of 100 kiloelectron volts (keV) to 1.02 megaelectron volts (MeV). In these interactions, a photon (incident photon) enters an atom and interacts with an electron in the outer orbital of an atom. Because the interaction has more energy than can be completely absorbed by the electron, it only absorbs enough energy to get ejected from the atom. The ejected electron is called a recoil electron. The remaining energy from the incident photon gets released from the atom as a low energy photon that scatters in a different direction. Because of the scattering of the low energy radiation emitted as a result of Compton interactions, it is called scatter radiation.

Compton Scatter

Compton scatter occurs when a gamma ray interacts with a free or loosely bound electron. During this interaction, some of the energy from the gamma ray is absorbed into the electron. The amount of energy absorbed depends on the angle of interaction between the gamma ray and electron. If they collide head on, the majority of the gamma ray's energy will be transferred to the electron. If the collision occurs at different angles, a lesser amount of energy will be transferred from the gamma ray to the electron. Compton scatter removes the electron from its orbit and results in a reduced-energy gamma ray.

Photoelectric Interactions of X-Radiation

The photoelectric interactions of x-radiation are relatively low-energy interactions that occur at energy levels of about 35 kilo electron volts (keV). During these interactions, a photon (incident photon) enters an atom and interacts with an inner shell electron. Although it is a relatively low-energy interaction, it does carry with it enough energy to eject the electron from its orbit. This is because the energy of the photon is greater than the binding energy of the electron that absorbs it. The ejected electron is called a photoelectron. Several things will occur once the photoelectron is ejected. It will quickly be absorbed by another atom, causing a reaction within that atom. The electrons from the outer orbitals of the original atom will move in to fill the void of the ejected electron. Because less energy is required to maintain position in the inner orbitals, the rearranged electrons will release energy in the form of low-energy photons that travel in different directions. The type of radiation that occurs as a result of photoelectric interactions is called secondary radiation because is it produced secondary to the initial interaction.

Photoelectric Effect

The photoelectric effect occurs when a gamma ray interacts with an electron on an inner orbit. During this interaction, the energy from the gamma ray is totally absorbed by the inner-orbit electron. The electron that absorbs the gamma ray is referred to as a photoelectron. The photoelectron is ejected from its orbit and the atom. The energy of the photoelectron is equal to the energy of the gamma ray minus the binding energy the electron needed to remain in its orbits. Due to the vacancy of an inner-orbit electron, outer-orbit electrons will drop down to fill the space left by the photoelectron and a series of x-rays will be emitted for every electron that changes orbit.

Coherent Interactions of X-Radiation

The coherent interactions of x-radiation are low-energy interactions that occur below 10 kilo electron volts (keV). During these interactions, a photon (incident photon) enters the orbital of an atom and interacts with an electron. Because these are low-energy interactions, the photon does not carry enough energy to eject the electron from the atom's orbit. Instead, the energy is absorbed and this excess energy causes the electron to vibrate (excitation). It eventually releases a photon of exactly the same energy as the absorbed one. This photon scatters in a different direction. Because of the scattering of radiation, this interaction is called scatter radiation.

Attenuation, Attenuator, Attenuation Profile, and Attenuation Coefficient

Attenuation is the reduction in the intensity of radiation when it passes through matter, whereupon that radiation is absorbed and scattered. **Attenuator** is the material or device used to reduce the intensity of x-ray or ultrasound. **Attenuation profile** is the result of the CT process that defines the attenuation properties of individual ray sums as they relate to the position of the ray. **Attenuation coefficient** is the numerical expression of a decrease in intensity that includes a penetration into matter. Also defined by the process of energy absorption, the attenuation coefficient describes the percent of radiation that remains after the x-rays pass through an object. It is expressed as an inverse length of m^{-1} or cm^{-1}.

Tissue Attenuation

As an x-ray beam passes through matter, it leaves energy behind. The result is the lessening (attenuation) of the beam strength. When the beam passes through tissue, the density of the tissue dictates how much radiation passes through, and how much gets absorbed. More of the beam gets absorbed by the dense tissue. This is because it blocks the beam from passing through. The denser the tissue, the lighter the image on the radiograph. Bones, for example, show up white on the radiograph. Other tissues are less dense and the beam passes through relatively unobstructed. When less of the beam gets absorbed, the resulting image is darker.

Pair Production Interactions of X-Radiation

Pair production interactions of x-radiation are high-energy interactions, occurring at energy levels of 1.02 to 10 megaelectron volts (MeV). In these interactions, a photon (incident photon) has enough energy to enter an atom and interact with the nucleus causing the photon to split into to two parts, a positron and a negatron. The negatron has just a small charge and will go on to be absorbed by another nearby atom. The positron, which carries most of the charge, will exit the atom and be attracted to an electron of another atom. This interaction is called an annihilation reaction because it causes the positron and electron to split into two high-energy photons. The photons will continue to interact with other atoms until all of the energy is absorbed. Because of the high energy levels used, this type of interaction can be found in radiation therapy (not diagnostic radiography).

Pair Production

Pair production occurs when a gamma ray reaches the vicinity of a nucleus. The energy of the gamma ray is totally absorbed by the electrical field of the nucleus, thus yielding the production of a beta particle and a positron. Pair production will only occur if the gamma ray has a minimum energy of 1.022 MeV. The beta particle travels until it is incorporated into an atom or acts as a free electron. The positron inevitably collides with an electron, resulting in annihilation of both particles and the emission of 2 gamma rays with 511 keV of energy.

Auger Electrons

Auger electrons are produced when an inner-shell electron is released from its orbit, leaving a vacancy. When there is a vacancy on an inner shell, outer-shell electrons adjust and move closer to the core, filling the vacancy. Every time an electron moves to a different shell, energy is released. Sometimes the energy is released in the form of a photon. Other times, the energy is transferred to an outer-shell electron, which is then released from the atom. An Auger electron is one that absorbs the energy and is subsequently released from the atom.

Half-Life and Half-Value Layer

The half-life of radioactive material is the amount of time necessary for it to decay to half of its original intensity. This is important knowledge when calculating dose for medical or occupational procedures. If a particular type of radioactive material has a half-life of 6 hours, then a 100mr dose of the material will have an intensity of just 50mr in six hours, and 25mr in 12 hours. Half-value layer is a term used in medical applications of radiation. It is defined as the amount of barrier material necessary to reduce the intensity of radiation by half. This is important when determining patient dose and devising radiation protection protocols.

Radioactive Decay

Radioactive decay is the result of the random collapse of radioactive isotopes that takes place within a nucleus that is considered to be unstable. These radioisotopes are attempting to modify the nucleus to transform into a stable isotope but tend to convert into an entirely different element during this process. The breakdown of the nucleus will emit radiation, but once it becomes stable, it is deemed as nonradioactive. To become stable, these atoms will keep giving off radiation, but the amount is decreased with each step. The half-life of a radioisotope is the amount of time that is necessary for the radioactivity of an isotope to drop to a value that is half of the original level of radioactivity. Radioisotopes do not all have the same decay rate. They do, however, show rates that are generally predictable for a specific type of isotope.

Alpha Decay

Alpha decay is a radioactive decay process in which the unstable atom emits an alpha particle in order to achieve stability. An alpha particle has an atomic structure identical to a helium atom—2 protons and 2 neutrons. Alpha particles are denoted by the Greek symbol α or the chemical formula for Helium nuclei, which is ${}^4{}_2He$. Alpha decay typically occurs in heavier atoms such as uranium-238 and the daughter atom is lighter than the parent atom by the amount of a helium atom. The decay of uranium-238 results in the daughter atom thorium-234 and an alpha particle. The alpha decay structure of uranium-238 is documented with the following decay equation:

$$^{238}_{92}U \rightarrow ^{234}_{90}Th + ^{4}_{2}He$$

Beta Decay

Beta decay is a radioactive decay process in which an unstable atom emits a beta particle in order to achieve stability. This form of decay can result in 2 different particles being emitted, either an electron or a positron. If an electron is emitted, the particle is referred to as a beta minus (β^-). If a positron is emitted, the particle is referred to as a beta plus (β^+). In beta minus decay, the atomic number of the daughter atom increases by 1. In beta plus decay, the atomic number of the daughter atom decreases by 1.

Gamma Decay

Gamma decay is unlike alpha, beta minus, or beta plus decay in that the atomic number of the parent and daughter atoms are identical. In alpha or beta decay, an atom is frequently left in an excited state. In order for the nucleus to remove itself from the excited state and return to the stable, ground state, it must emit energy. The energy emitted from these nuclei is in the form of photons referred to as gamma rays. For isotopes that use gamma decay, all photons that are emitted contain the same energy and ionization properties.

Physical Half-Life

Physical half-life, also referred to as radioactive half-life, is the amount of time it takes for the original number of atoms in a radioactive sample to be reduced by 50%. This may also be referred to as radioactive decay and is a characteristic of all radioactive materials. Each radioactive isotope has a different rate of decay or half-life. However, the rate of decay for each radioisotope in constant and cannot be altered by outside influences such as temperature or pressure.

Biological Half-Life

Biological half-life is defined as the amount of time it takes the body to eliminate half the quantity of any substance, not just radioactivity. Biological half-life is the same for both stable and radioactive forms of any element. The body's main methods of eliminating substances are genitourinary excretion, gastrointestinal excretion, exhalation, and perspiration.

Effective Half-Life

Effective half-life is defined as the amount of time required to reduce the quantity of a substance in the body when both physical and biological half-life are taken into consideration. Effective half-life combines the action of radioactive decay and natural elimination. Effective half-life can be calculated in the following equation:

$$\frac{1}{t_{eff}} = \frac{1}{t_{biol}} + \frac{1}{t_{phys}}$$

Biological Aspects of Radiation

Overall Biological Effects of Radiation

The overall bioeffects of radiation are a random process that may or may not result in biological (or chemical) changes in an organism. During exposure, the energy of radiation enters cells both very quickly and randomly. There is no way to predict which cells will be affected by irradiation. However, the chances of biological harm as a result of a radiation application increase with the amount of energy to which one is exposed. This could mean either a higher dose or a longer application time. The negative effects of radiation are detectable only after time and in the form of a different disease. This is called the "latent period" and can last weeks, months, or years. These negative effects, however, can be difficult to pin down to radiation exposure because there is no disease that is specifically a result of irradiation. Many diseases caused by radiation exposure could also have been caused by other factors.

Relationship Between Radiation Exposure and Carcinogenisis

There are different ways in which a person can be exposed to radiation: medical exposure, occupational exposure, accidents or disasters. The different types of exposure yield varying doses, and the relationship between these varying doses and types of exposure to the development of cancer has been studied. There is a correlation between radiation exposure and cancer. The effect, however, is random (or stochastic). That is, a person may or may not develop cancer as a result of exposure. The chances of developing cancer do increase with exposure, however the degree of severity of the disease does not necessarily increase. It is all an "all or nothing" response, where an individual either does or does not develop cancer. The development of caner due to exposure at any level is described as a linear nonthreshold dose-effect response because it is not known just how much radiation can result in cancer development. Thus, any level of radiation exposure technically has the capability of producing cancer.

Direct and Indirect Action Regarding Cellular Effects of Radiation

Direct action refers to cellular damage in response to direct absorption of ionizing radiation. This type of ionization occurs at all levels of radiation. The greater the exposure to radiation, the greater the amount of cellular damage. Indirect action refers to the production of a free radical as a result of radiation exposure. A free radical is an electrically neutral atom with an unoccupied electron. Since the primary atom in the body is water, radiation exposure can break water down into a hydrogen atom ($H+$) and a hydroxide ion (OH^-). When many of these hydroxide ion free radicals are present in the body, the formation of toxic hydrogen peroxide (H_2O_2) may result.

Skin Entrance Dose, Gonadal Dose, and Bone Marrow Dose

Entrance skin dose is a measurement of the mount of radiation at the level of the patient's skin. This measurement is a sum of the intended dose and the scatter radiation as the beam reaches the patient. It is an important part of determining the effective dose. Gonadal dose and bone marrow dose are approximate measurements of the amount of radiation that each of those regions is exposed to during a radiographic procedure. Although they are just estimates, these dose amounts are important because the gonads and bone marrow are highly radiosensitive regions of the body and unnecessary exposure of these regions can lead to serious health problems.

Units of Measure for Radiation Exposure

There are three basic measures of radiation exposure—roentgen (R), radiation absorbed dose (rad), and radiation equivalent to man (rem). Roentgen, a term applied to x-rays and gamma rays, is the amount of radiation it takes to produce 1 electrostatic charge in 1cc of dry air at standard temperature and pressure. Rad differs from roentgen in that it encompasses all types of radiation, not just x-rays and gamma rays. In addition, rad can be measured in types of matter other than air. Rem is the unit of measure applied to radiation exposure in humans. It is calculated by multiplying the number of rads by the relative biologic effectiveness (RBE).

Rad

The rad, as a unit of measurement, is an acronym that stands for radiation absorbed dose and is used to quantify patient dose. It can be used to quantify any type of radiation and measures the amount of energy that is absorbed (deposited) in tissue per unit mass. It correlates to chemical change and biological damage because the greater the amount of radiation absorbed, the greater the possibility for chemical change that can result in biological damage. The rad is a conventional unit of measure and conventional units are typically used in radiation measurement. Some reports, however, do use SI units and so radiographers need to be familiar with these units as well. The SI unit for the rad is the gray (Gy). 100 rad = 1 gray.

Rem

The rem, as a unit of measurement, is an acronym that stands for radiation equivalent man and is used to quantify occupational exposure. It can be used to measure any type of radiation and uses the information gathered for the rad (radiation absorbed dose) but incorporates a quality factor (QF) that predicts the potential biological effects of different types of radiation. Because the rem incorporates a quality factor that relates to different types of radiation, it is an effective measurement tool for occupational exposure where an individual uses and is potentially exposed to many different types of radiation. The rem is a conventional unit of measure and conventional units are typically used in radiation measurement. Some reports, however, do use SI units and so radiographers need to be familiar with these units as well. The SI unit for the rem is the sievert (Sv). 100 rem = 1 sievert.

Effective Dose

Effective dose is one way to estimate the risk involved in a certain exposure to ionizing radiation. It takes into consideration the radiosensitivity of the tissue being exposed and the type of radiation applied. It is calculated from the following formula:

Effective dose (E) = Radiation weighing factor (Wr) x Tissue weighing factor (Wt) x Absorbed dose

Radiation weighing factor is a value given to the type of radiation (x, gamma, alpha, beta) based on its potential for biological effects. Tissue weighing factors reflect the radiosensitivity of the tissue being irradiated. Absorbed dose is also called skin entrance dose and is the dose that is actually absorbed by the patient (intended dose plus scatter radiation).

Weight Factor

Since radiation exposure for clinical procedures is generally localized to only certain parts of the body, one needs to be able to more accurately calculate the effect of the dose given to the entire body and the probability that it will result in mutations. For this reason, weight factors were devised so that the exposure to individual tissues could be weighted and the appropriate dose calculated. This helps to minimize the risk of negative effects of radiation. Gonads have a weight factor of 0.25, breasts 0.15, red bone marrow 0.12, lung 0.12, thyroid 0.03, and bone surface 0.30. Organs with higher radiosensitivity have a correspondingly higher weight factor. In order to translate the dose that a particular portion of the body received into a whole body dose, you need to multiply the dose given by the weight factor. For example, if 20 mrad of radiation were applied to the thyroid (weight factor of 0.03), the total whole body dose would only be 0.60mrad.

Effects of Radiation Exposure on Lymphocytes, Epithelial Tissue, and Nerve Cells

Lymphocytes are white blood cells that are a part of the immune system and play an important role in a body's defense against infection. They are highly radiosensitive and so can easily be affected by radiation exposure. If radiation exposure results in harm to the lymphocytes, the body's immune system becomes compromised and a person easily becomes susceptible to infection and disease. Epithelial tissue, which can be found in the lining of the intestines and respiratory system, is also a highly radiosensitive tissue. Damage to these cells is a major complication in acute radiation syndrome. Nerve cells in adults are the most radioresistant cells in the body. They do not undergo cell division, and so are less at risk for undergoing biological change due to radiation exposure. This is not the case, however, in fetal nerve cells. The fetus is, in general, highly radiosensitive because there is much cell division and differentiation as a part of fetal development.

Dose-Response Relationships

Dose-response (or effect) relationships describe the relationship between the amount of radiation applied (dose) and the biological effect (response) to an organism. This relationship is categorized as either linear or nonlinear. A linear relationship means that the biological effect is directly proportional to the dose applied. In these cases, if the dose is doubled, then so too is the biological effect. In a nonlinear relationship (sometimes called curvilinear or quadratic), however, dose and effect are not directly proportional. The term "threshold" is applied to both linear and nonlinear relationships to define the dose below which no negative effects of radiation are detected.

Linear Threshold and Nonthreshold Curves of Dose-Response

In linear dose-response relationships, dose and response are directly proportional to each other. If a linear relationship is threshold-dependent, then the dose of radiation must reach some minimum amount before there are any negative effects. In a linear nonthreshold dose-response, there is no response to the dose until it reaches a certain level, after which a response is indicated. The linear nonthreshold curve is used to describe the relationship between radiation dose and the occurrence of radiation-induced cancers and genetic effects. These effects are considered random (or stochastic) and there is no predictable dose before which they may occur. For this reason, the linear nonthreshold curve cannot be applied. Because there are negative effects to radiation exposure that occur without threshold, the linear nonthreshold curve is used in prescribing radiation protection.

Nonlinear Threshold and Nonthreshold Curves of Dose-Response

In nonlinear dose-response relationships, dose and response are not directly proportional. A typical nonlinear curve is the nonlinear threshold "S" curve, also called the "sigmoid" curve. It represents cases where a great amount of radiation is necessary before an effect is seen, but then only small amounts thereafter produce an effect. Non-stochastic (or predictable) effects of radiation exposure fall into this category. A nonlinear nonthreshold dose-response describes instances where the dose is not proportional to the effect and there is no minimum dose-response threshold.

RBE

The term "relative biological effectiveness" (RBE) is a way of quantifying the amount of damage radiation can do in relative terms. x, gamma, and alpha radiation are all types of ionizing radiation, but differ in their wavelengths and frequencies, and thus have different degrees of penetrating power. Alpha radiation has the highest degree of penetrating power and so has the greatest potential to do harm to biological systems. RBE allows one to determine the possible effects of alpha radiation compared to the same quantity of x-radiation.

Relative Biologic Effectiveness refers to the fact that different types of radiation produce different biologic effects. RBE primarily is the ratio of an absorbed dose of x-rays or gamma rays to the amount of any other form of radiation that is needed to produce the same biologic effect. RBE is calculated by the following formula:

$$RBE = \frac{\text{Dose of x} - \text{ray or gamma radiation}}{\text{Equivalent dose of radiation in question}}$$

For example, if 0.05 rad of alpha radiation produces the same effect as 1 rad of gamma radiation, the RBE for alpha radiation would be the following:

$$RBE = \frac{1\,rad}{0.05\,rad} = 20$$

LET

Linear energy transfer (LET) is defined as the average amount of energy deposited to a medium by ionizing radiation as it passes through it relative to the linear distance traveled by the energy. The damage to cells caused by radiation exposure is a result of the deposit of energy into cells and the subsequent biological or chemical change that occurs. Some of these effects are more harmful than others, with some having long-term permanent effects, and others resulting in death. Radiation with a higher LET has the potential to deposit more energy. There are two basic types of ionizing radiation: wave (gamma and x-rays) and particulate (alphas and betas). Particle radiation has a higher LET and therefore has the greater possibility of causing harmful effects to an organism.

Relative Tissue Radiosensitivity

Relative tissue radiosensitivity says that the radiosensitivity of any tissue is relative to the cellular composition of the tissue. It uses the "Bergonie-Tribondeau law" which consists of three principles for determining tissue radiosensitivity. They are: the more mitotic activity (cell division), the less differentiated (a cell without a specific purpose), and the higher the oxygen content at the time of radiation exposure, the more radiosensitive the cell or tissue. Lymphocytes, blood-forming cells, germ cells (egg and sperm), and the lens of the eye have high radiosensitivity. Growing bone and cartilage, epithelial cells of the kidney, liver, pancreas, thyroid, and adrenal glands have moderate radiosensitivity. Muscle tissue, mature bone or cartilage, and nerve tissue all have low radiosensitivity.

Direct Effects of Radiation at the Cellular Level

Radiation has a direct effect at a cellular level when a photon enters a cell and ionizes a macromolecule within that cell. The ionized macromolecule does not function properly and this, in turn, affects the way the cell functions as a whole. The damage to the macromolecule may cause physical or chemical changes within the cell. The result of such an effect is that the macromolecule may die, or because the function of the cell is compromised, the entire cell may die.

Indirect Effects of Radiation at the Cellular Level

Indirect effects of radiation occur when a photon irradiates the water within a cell. The ionized water molecule breaks apart to form an unstable water molecule and a free electron. The free electron can then bond with another water molecule, producing a second unstable water molecule. The bonds of unstable molecules are easily broken. When this happens, a free radical is produced. Free radicals can themselves cause damage to the cell by interfering with cellular function or cause the production of chemicals harmful to the cell. The end result is death of the cell or a change in cellular function.

LD 50/30

Radiation exposure can result in a shortening of a person's natural life span. This is because radiation has the potential of speeding up the natural process of aging through tissue damage and degeneration, as well as causing the premature development of diseases. It has been determined that there is a lethal dose of radiation that will result in the death of 50% of the population within 30 days of exposure. This is called LD 50/30 and is a much higher dose than is seen through typical occupational exposure. The approximate lethal dose for humans has been estimated to be between 250-450 rad.

Oxygen Effect

Radiosensitivity refers to how effectively and quickly a tumor responds to therapeutic radiation and/or anticancer treatments. There are many influencers that must be considered when optimal radiosensitivity is the desired result, such as size of the tumor, growth, and cell cycling. Another important component to consider is the oxygen effect. The oxygen effect is considered during oncology treatment as tumors that are hypoxic (low oxygen supply) or anoxic (no oxygen supply) are often unaffected by ionizing radiation and chemotherapy drugs and, therefore, have less radiosensitivity. In fact, radiation therapy is roughly one-third as effective to cells that are considered to be anoxic when compared to cells that have a good supply of oxygen when exposed to ionizing radiation. Much research is being done to increase the oxygen levels during irradiation as the oxygen has to be raised only for a very brief time during the radiation exposure for the cell to heighten the level of radiosensitivity.

Effects of Radiation Exposure on Reproductive System

Radiation exposure can have an effect on the germ cells of an organism (the sperm and egg). This can have a direct effect on an individual's reproductive ability. Sperm and eggs can be damaged at an exposure of 200 rad, causing temporary sterility. Sometime sterility is permanent. A dose of 500-600 rad can cause permanent sterility in men or women. If germ cells survive radiation exposure but are somehow damaged and become a part of procreation, it can result in miscarriage or birth defects.

Short-Term Versus Long-Term Effects of Radiation Exposure to Somatic Cells

A somatic cell is any cell in the body, excluding reproductive cells (egg or sperm). Somatic effects of radiation exposure are effects that directly damage the body at a cellular level, but are not capable of being passed on to future generations. The short-term effects to these cells are experienced less than 30 days after exposure, are sudden, and are not permanent. Some short-term effects to somatic cells are redness of the exposed skin and hair loss. These effects are often seen in patients after radiation treatment. Long-term effects due to radiation exposure occur 30 days or more after exposure, have a slow onset, worsen over, time, and are permanent and sometimes fatal. Cancer and cataracts are examples of long-term effects to somatic cells. Cancer is described as a stochastic (random) linear nonthreshold effect, whereas cataracts are nonstochastic (predictable) nonlinear threshold effects from a collective chronic exposure.

Acute Versus Chronic Effects of Radiation

The effects of radiation exposure can be classified as either acute or chronic and the difference between the two depends on the amount of radiation dose over time. Acute effects (called acute radiation syndrome) result from large doses of radiation over a short period of time. These effects are essentially short-term effects because the damage to the body from exposure is so great that the short-term outcome is death (usually within 30 days). Conversely, chronic effects are a result of a large amount of radiation delivered in small doses over a long period of time. These are the long-term effects of radiation exposure that often don't surface for years and are the ones most likely to be found in a diagnostic radiation setting. Some of these effects include genetic effects, cataracts, leukemia, and cancers.

Sensitivity of Eyes, Bone Marrow, and Thyroid to Radiation Exposure

The sensitivity of the eyes, bone marrow, and thyroid to radiation exposure is described below:

- Eyes: Repeated exposure to radiation in low doses has been shown to increase a person's risk for developing cataracts. This is a cumulative, chronic effect that is best characterized as a nonlinear threshold response.
- Bone Marrow: Bone marrow contains the stem cells that make red blood cells and these are very radiosensitive. Either acute (large dose over a short time) or chronic (small doses over a long time) doses can result in a disruption of the blood-forming system (hematopoietic system).
- Thyroid: The thyroid is very close to the surface in the neck and is highly radiosensitive. Small doses (50 rad) have been shown to result in thyroid tumors.

Acute Radiation Syndrome

Acute Radiation Syndrome is the condition that is caused from exposure to high levels of radiation over a short period of time. This time frame is generally less than 24 hours. There are three periods (or phases) of the syndrome. The Prodromal Period, the first phase, lasts 24 hours after exposure and is characterized by nausea, vomiting, loss of appetite, and apathy. The second phase is the Latent Period and is characterized by the absence of all symptoms. The third phase is the Manifest

Period and this is the point at which the body reacts to the damaging effects of radiation exposure. The symptoms are often lumped together as "radiation sickness." Radiation sickness, however, can be grouped into three different categories based on the system that it affects. These are hematopoietic syndrome, gastrointestinal syndrome, and central nervous system syndrome.

CATEGORIES OF RADIATION SICKNESS

The three major categories of radiation sickness are hematopoietic syndrome, gastrointestinal syndrome, and central nervous system syndrome. Hematopoietic syndrome occurs at the relatively lowest dose (100-1000 rad) because the hematopoietic (blood-forming) system is the most sensitive to radiation exposure. There is a decrease in red blood cells, white blood cells, and clotting cells, resulting in a decrease in immune response and blood clotting ability. An individual may die within 30 days from secondary disease or hemorrhage. Gastrointestinal syndrome occurs at exposures of 600-1000 rad. The lining of the gastrointestinal system is damaged, resulting in the abnormal function of the GI tract. Individuals experience nausea, vomiting, ulcerations, and hemorrhage and may die within 10-14 days. Central nervous system syndrome occurs at the highest levels of radiation exposure: 2000-5000rad. Symptoms include confusion, disorientation, ataxia (wobbliness) and an increase in intracranial pressure, as well as seizures, agitation, and shock. Death usually occurs within 14-36 hours.

EMBRYONIC AND FETAL RISKS ASSOCIATED WITH RADIATION EXPOSURE

The embryonic and fetal risks associated with radiation exposure depend greatly on gestational period. During the first trimester, there is the greatest risk of negative effects to the embryo. Embryonic cells at this stage are the most radiosensitive because they are in a state of rapid division and are not yet differentiated. Thus, radiation can cause the most damage to a proportionally larger number of cells and can even result in the death of the embryo. During the second trimester, embryonic cells are still considered highly radiosensitive, however, because cells have by now differentiated into their respective organs, the effect is not as great as with the first trimester. Embryonic death is not likely at this point, but severe deformities are. The third trimester represents the period during which the fetus is the most radioresistant. Effects at this point are usually to the central nervous system and can be seen in the child as a low IQ or neurological problems.

GENETIC EFFECTS OF RADIATION

Genetic effects occur only when the DNA of germ cells (egg or sperm) is damaged. The effects can be either a mutation in a single base pair in the DNA (point mutation) or as a mutation to a larger portion of the chromosome. Chromosomal mutations are the most common genetic effects, occurring 90% of the time. These mutations can be classified into two groups: single strand, one break or single strand, double break. Single strand, one break mutations can be terminal deletions, inversions, or duplication. Single strand, double breaks occur when there are two breaks on the same chromosome. They can be caused by insertion deletion, inversion, duplication, or translocation.

GENETICALLY SIGNIFICANT DOSE AND DOUBLING DOSE

Radiation exposure to reproductive organs (especially the gonads) can result in temporary or permanent sterility. It can also result in genetic effects. Genetic effects are effects of radiation to germ cells (sperm and egg) that are then used in procreation. These effects are seen, not in the parents, but in their offspring. A genetically significant dose is the dose that would cause a significant increase in genetic effects in humans. The genetically significant dose is estimated to be approximately 20 rad. A doubling dose is described as the dose necessary to double the number of genetic mutations that occur in nature. The doubling dose in humans is estimated to be 50-250 rad.

Stochastic Effects of Radiation

Stochastic effects of radiation are generally associated with exposure to low-level radiation over a prolonged period of time. Long-term exposure to low-level radiation can lead to leukemia and other forms of cancer. This type of radiation exposure can also alter human genetics—causing chromosome damage, for example—due to its effects at the cellular level. Genetic effects of this kind are difficult to quantify, however. Long-term, low-level radiation exposure has been associated with genetic birth defects, too, but it is extremely difficult to determine what percentage of those are related to radiation exposure.

Deterministic Effects of Radiation

Deterministic effects of radiation can also be referred to as non-stochastic radiation effects. Deterministic effects are a result of a high dose of radiation over a short period of time. These types of effects are directly proportional to the amount of radiation exposure. The greater the amount of radiation exposure, the more severe the biological effect. Deterministic effects can vary from redness of the skin to death in some cases. Depending on the dose of radiation absorbed, deterministic events can be immediate, as with very high levels of radiation, or may take a few days to develop, as might occur with relatively low levels of radiation.

Minimizing Patient Exposure

Exposure Factors

Exposure factors are the combination of factors that, when all are taken into consideration, yield a clear radiograph at the lowest patient dose. The quality and quantity of radiation beam must be such that it minimizes a patient's risk of unnecessary exposure to the potentially harmful effects of radiation. There are two factors that are adjusted to get the appropriate patient dose. These are the kilovoltage peak (kVp) and milliampere-seconds (mAs). A high kVp and low mAs usually result in the least amount of patient exposure. This is because with a high kVp, more of the radiation passes through the individual, as opposed to being absorbed; and with a low mAs, the individual is exposed to a small amount of radiation over a longer time, which causes less harm to the body than a larger amount of radiation over a short time.

KVp

The term "kVp" stands for kilovoltage peak and is a measurement of the penetrating ability of the radiation dose. With a higher kVp, more of the radiation passes through the patient to the film that needs to be exposed. This means that less of the radiation is absorbed by the patient and the risk of biological harm is reduced. If the kVp is too high, however, then there will be secondary scatter radiation. This is low energy radiation that is easily absorbed by the patient, and so actually increases the risk of excessive exposure. The scatter radiation will also result in a radiograph that is difficult to read (because of background noise), making it necessary to repeat the procedure, and unnecessarily expose the patient again. The area of the body being exposed determines the kVp. A large bone, that requires more penetrating power, requires a higher kVp than a small bone.

Generators

There are three types of generators used in producing radiographs: single-phase, three-phase, and high-frequency. A single-phase generator produces a gradual rise in voltage from 0, to its peak, then back down to 0 again. This means that photons with a wide range of energy are produced. Low-energy photons do not have enough penetrating power to produce an image, thus are absorbed by the body and risk biological harm. A three-phase generator still produces some low-energy radiation, but greatly reduced from the single-phase generator. A high-frequency generator produces a consistently energized beam (monoenergetic) and so has the smallest amount of voltage drop. It produces very little low-energy radiation and thus greatly reduces the patient dosage.

HALF-THICKNESS

The ability of any material to shield against ionizing radiation exposure is determined by the amount (thickness) of the material necessary to absorb half of the radiation. This is called the "half-thickness" of the material. When ionizing radiation passes through one half-thickness, half of the radiation is absorbed and the other half passes through. If this remaining half passes through a second half-thickness, half of that energy will be absorbed, leaving only a quarter of the original beam to pass through. The half-thickness value of any material is based on the characteristics of the material and the type of radiation for which it is meant to be a barrier.

BEAM RESTRICTION

The purpose of beam restriction is to target the x-ray beam to the area being imaged, and only that area. This reduces patient exposure in two ways. Because only the relevant area is exposed to radiation, the patient dose is kept to a minimum. It also limits the amount of off-focus scatter radiation produced by the x-ray tube. When scatter radiation is produced, it reduces the quality of the image and increases the exposure of the patient and personnel to low-energy ionizing radiation that is easily absorbed by the body. This is contrary to the ALARA Principle (as low as reasonably achievable) and should be avoided.

FILTRATION

The purpose of filtration in radiography is the removal of the low-energy photons from the x-ray beam as it leaves the tube. Low-energy photons are the non-penetrating radiation that is either absorbed by the patient, increasing the risk of harmful biological effects, or a source of background noise, diminishing the quality of the radiograph. There are three ways that filtration may be applied to the beam. If it is a part of the actual tube (such as oil, Pyrex glass, tube window), it is called "inherent filtration." If it is an object placed in the pathway of the beam (such as collimator mirror) it is called "added filtration." The last is "total filtration," which describes the filtering properties of both inherent and added filtration used in combination.

INHERENT FILTRATION AND ADDED FILTRATION

Inherent filters are radiation filtration mechanisms that are built into the x-ray equipment. They act to filter out the low-energy photons that would be absorbed by the patient. Some of the inherent filters in radiographic equipment are a Pyrex glass window, oil coolant, collimator, and collimator mirror. At low enough doses (less than 50 kVp), these filters may be sufficient to meet the NRCP guidelines for filtration. Added filters are the thin sheets of metal (typically aluminum) that is added to the equipment to bring up the total filtration to meet NRCP guidelines. This is particularly necessary when the x-ray equipment is operating at settings higher than 70 kVp and a total filtration of 2.5 mm Al equivalent is recommended.

QUALITY MANAGEMENT PROGRAMS

A quality management program is of great importance for facilities that perform radioactive therapeutic procedures. The purpose of a quality management program is to reduce the risk of administration errors and reportable events. There are 5 main objectives essential to any quality management program.

1. A written directive is obtained prior to administration of any radioactive material.
2. The patient is verified with more than one method.
3. All calculations and courses of treatment follow the written directive.

4. The radioactive material is administered according to the written directive.
5. Appropriate action is taken if deviation from the written directive occurs.

Written Directives

A written directive is needed when administering any therapeutic dose of radioactive material. A written directive is not required when administering radioactive materials for diagnostic purposes. Prior to administering a therapeutic dose, a written directive must be obtained and it must contain the following information.

1. The patient's name
2. The name, dose, and route of administration of the radioactive material
3. The purpose for the administration of radioactive materials
4. The date and time of the administration of radioactive materials
5. The signature of the authorized user performing or overseeing the administration of radioactive material

Retaining Department Records

3 Years

All records of department wipe tests and surveys; all dose calibrator evaluations such as linearity, constancy, and accuracy; all records of patient dose administrations, both diagnostic and therapeutic; all written directives; all records of radioactive trash decayed and disposed of; receipts for all radioactive shipments.

5 Years

All records of radioactive materials transferred from one facility to another; the department inventory of all sealed sources including flood sources, radioactive markers, and attenuation correction sources; all leak tests that have been performed on the inventory of sealed sources; records of all administration errors.

Indefinitely

All records of personnel radiation exposure; all minutes from radiation safety committee meetings (these are kept indefinitely or for the duration of the radioactive materials license); dose calibrator geometry evaluations (these are kept indefinitely or for the life of the dose calibrator); all records of I-131 bioassays performed on radiation workers.

Importance of Patient Communication in Minimizing Exposure

Patient cooperation during any radiographic procedure is essential in producing a high quality radiograph. Aspects of the procedure such as positioning and eliminating movement greatly rely on the patient understanding their role in the procedure. For this reason, it is important that the radiographer thoroughly explain to the patient the procedure and what is expected of them. A radiographer may encounter many obstacles to communication, such as the elderly with impaired mobility or hearing, non-English-speaking patients, pediatric patients, physically or mentally impaired, or those seriously ill, injured, or traumatized. It is necessary to adjust communication style to adequately meet the needs of any of these patients. Appropriate and complete communication with patients yields a better radiograph and helps to reduce the need for unnecessary repeat exposure. Repeat exposure accounts for a significant amount of unnecessary patient exposure.

Effect of Filtration Measures on Beam Energy and Patient Dose

Filtration measures result in the removal of low-energy photons from the x-ray beam leaving the tube. Since these low-energy photons are removed from the equation before the beam ever reaches the patient, the average beam energy is increased. The filter, instead of the patient, absorbs the low-energy photons. Thus, while the average beam energy is increased with filtration, the dosage to the patient's skin and organs is reduced. The overall effect is a high quality beam that penetrates the patient to expose the radiographic film without producing damaging effects to the patient.

Impact of Morbid Obesity on Patient Exposure

Technologists must be knowledgeable when examining morbidly obese patients to provide quality diagnostic exams and prevent repeat studies. More scatter radiation results from excess tissue found in the obese patient population. Collimation of the anatomy of interest is one method that technologists can utilize to improve diagnostic quality and decrease the amount of scatter stemming from the patient. Technologists should make sure that the kVp and mAs are optimally set to improve the contrast of the image. Technologists must determine if grids are necessary and adjust the output settings when in use. Sometimes, more than one exposure will be necessary to cover the area of interest, so it is important to plan ahead to reduce the amount of radiographic views taken. Technologists should also be aware of additional methods for locating anatomical landmarks to prevent repeat exposures as palpation may not always be possible.

Effects of Image Receptors on Patient Exposure

It is imperative for technologists to understand the selections of image receptors (IR) and how they affect patient exposure. It is important to choose the image receptor that allows for optimal diagnostic quality. Although digital image receptors do not have a set reactivity or film speed, all exposure monitors still need to be verified to control the amount of ionizing radiation that the patient is subjected to. They do, however, produce quality images that expand over broad exposure settings. Grids are useful to boost the contrast during exams but should also be carefully selected along with the correct exposure techniques. Grids are known to double some exposure techniques, so eliminating grids during pediatric exams is useful. Grids that enable scatter radiation from the patient to contribute to the image are considered to be low ratio. These grids can utilize lower techniques. High-ratio grids tend to raise the amount of exposure to the patient. Intensifying screens that contribute less X-ray dosage to the patient tend to provide clinicians with less quality because they tend to deliver images that are blurrier.

Gating

Technologists must always keep the as low as reasonably achievable (ALARA) principle in mind when performing exams. However, with the advancements of newer technology, some modalities have created an increase in patient dose. Newer cardiac applications, such as coronary artery CTA, have provided physicians with ample information. This has come about by requiring a significant increase of radiation dose to the patient. Two types of gating are used to acquire data during cardiac CT exams. Retrospective gating was the first method utilized that collected images during all phases of the cardiac cycle. Only the images that were necessary for a diagnosis were kept. Prospective gating is a technique used today that is used in conjunction with an electrocardiogram (EKG) to considerably reduce the amount of radiation to the patient. With this method, the patient is only exposed during the mid-diastolic portion of the cardiac cycle. Individuals who have a slower heart rate can be exposed to less radiation as the tube is only on during the contraction portion and can be turned off during the relaxation phase.

Personnel Protection (ALARA)

ICANL

The Intersocietal Commission for the Accreditation of Nuclear Medicine Laboratories (ICANL) is an accrediting body that imposes standards for nuclear cardiology, nuclear medicine, and PET facilities that must be met for accreditation. Accreditation is extremely important because many insurance reimbursements are based on procedures being performed at accredited facilities. Facilities that are not accredited may not be reimbursed for procedures performed at those facilities.

ACR

The American College of Radiology (ACR) is an accrediting body that imposes standards for nuclear cardiology, nuclear medicine, PET facilities, and all other imaging modalities such as CT and MRI. ACR standards must be met to obtain accreditation. Accreditation is extremely important for imaging facilities because many insurance reimbursements are based on procedures being performed at accredited facilities. Facilities that are not accredited may not be reimbursed for procedures performed at those facilities.

NRC

The Nuclear Regulatory Commission (NRC) was established by the US government to provide legislation pertaining to nuclear medicine (as well as nuclear power plants). This regulatory agency not only protects the public health sector but also the environment through the creation of guidelines to eliminate any unnecessary risk of exposure. The offices of the NRC are responsible for the supervision of emergency response protocols, licenses, inspections, and any regulatory oversight. These regulations apply to nuclear power plants and industrial and medical providers to operate while practicing correct handling, usage, and storage procedures. The NRC does not give instruction to patients regarding nuclear medicine or other therapeutic treatments performed. This information must be provided by the clinician.

MIPPA Law

The Medicare Improvements for Patients and Providers Act (MIPPA) is a piece of 2008 legislation that requires all non-hospital centers of advanced diagnostic imaging to obtain accreditation from the American College of Radiology (ACR) or the Intersocietal Commission for the Accreditation of Nuclear Medicine Laboratories (ICANL) by January 2012. This law does not only apply to nuclear medicine facilities. It applies to all forms of advanced diagnostic imaging, such as CT and MRI.

DAP Meter

Dose area product (DAP) meters are tools used to measure the amount of dose the patient has received during an X-ray exam. This equipment consists of an ionization compartment that is attached to the X-ray collimator so that the entire beam can be measured. This chamber automatically adjusts to the size of the radiation field. The DAP is calculated by multiplying the dose of radiation at the external portion of the body by the actual skin's surface area where the beam enters the body. These monitors are useful as the measurements can be changed when the technologist changes the size of the imaging field or modifies the techniques on the equipment (kVp and mAs). DAP meters are believed to be an accurate predictor of cancer because of exposure to radiation and a better measurement than just using entrance dose.

ALARA

ALARA stands for As Low As Reasonably Achievable. This principle is aimed at reducing radiation exposure in individuals who work routinely with radiation. ALARA is achieved by using protective equipment such as syringe shields, lead glass and lead shields. Reducing contact time with and maintaining distance from radioactive sources, including patients in a nuclear medicine setting, will also help keep radiation exposure as low as reasonably achievable.

Declaration of Pregnancy by a Radiation Worker

A female radiation worker has the right to declare a pregnancy at any time during the pregnancy. If she chooses not to declare the pregnancy, no measures need to be taken and the facility is not responsible for the safety of the fetus. If she declares the pregnancy, she must do so in writing and include the approximate date of impregnation. In addition, a fetal badge must be issued and worn in the abdominal region to quantify radiation exposure to the fetus, which must not exceed 500 mrem for the total duration of the pregnancy.

Patient as a Source of Radiation Exposure

Technologists must be aware that the majority of their occupational exposure is actually the result of scatter radiation from the patient. Scatter radiation stems from Compton events that take place in the body. Scatter radiation comes into contact with a patient or other objects while originating from the primary beam creating deflections in various directions. One of the main issues with scatter radiation stemming from patients is when technologists are holding the patient during an exposure. Scatter radiation is random, and the direction cannot be predicted, but it has been determined that most of the divergence occurs backward and to the side of the patient. Typically, when technologists are holding patients they are standing to the patient's side. It is important that lead aprons and gloves are utilized when it is necessary to hold a patient. During portable or fluoroscopy exams, the technologist should stand at least six feet away from the tube and make sure the fluoroscopy curtain is in place and always use the radiologist as a shield when possible.

Time as a Form of Protection from Radiation

Individuals are exposed to radiation on a daily basis whether it stems from diagnostic testing (X-ray, CT, nuclear medicine) or from natural sources such as the sun and radioactive elements or gasses. Radiology professionals should be cognizant of the concepts of time, distance, and shielding as basic radiographic safety protocols. Technologists should limit the amount of time spent in fluoroscopic procedures whenever possible as this will decrease their exposure. Departments with several staff should be sure that all staff rotate through fluoroscopy and surgical rotations. Staff should not hold patients during radiology procedures if at all possible to limit the time that they are exposed to the beam. All staff should wear their monitoring devices to track exposure levels. Homes should be tested for radon, which is a naturally occurring gas found in soil and water. Radon mitigation systems can be installed in homes to reduce the level of exposure to an acceptable level.

Effects of Distance from Radioactive Sources on ALARA

Maintaining distance from a radioactive source is one of the most effective and least expensive ways to reduce radiation exposure. The "inverse square law" tells us that if the distance from a radioactive source is doubled, the radiation exposure is one-fourth of that at the original distance. Conversely, if the distance from a radioactive source is halved, the radiation exposure is 4 times greater than at the original distance.

Signs Posted to Warn of Radioactivity

Several types of warning signs are posted in medical settings. These signs must accurately identify the type of radiation that may be encountered. A "Caution Radioactive Materials" sign posted 30 cm from the radiation source is sufficient for areas with a radiation level below 5 mR/hr. A "Caution Radiation Area" sign must be posted 30 cm from the radiation source or radioactive surface in all areas that have a radiation level greater than 5 mR/hr. A "Caution High Radiation Area" sign is required in all areas in which the radiation level exceeds 100 mR/hr. This, too, should be posted 30 cm from the radiation source or radioactive surface.

Attenuation Properties of Common Protective Devices

Attenuation takes place when there is a decrease in the intensity of the primary X-ray beam as it passes through materials. This may be due to the scattering of the primary beam or even the absorption of the beam by the patient. There are types of personal protective equipment used during radiology procedures. These include aprons, thyroid shields, lead gloves, and goggles—all typically made of lead. Lead is extremely heavy, so nonlead-based materials have been utilized to prevent any MSK injuries to technologists that are required to wear aprons for extended periods of time. Lead equivalent is a term that is used by shielding manufacturers when providing information pertaining to the protective properties of the products. The lead-based protective wear is supposed to be 0.35 mm and 0.50 mm thick and has decreased the exposure of more than 16 times in the total effective body dose. Thyroid shields have shown to decrease the total effective dose as well. Lead goggles have shown to restrict the amount of dose to the lens of the eye by attenuating the beam by 70%.

Image Production

Image Acquisition and Technical Evaluation

Selection of Technical Factors Affecting Radiographic Quality

It is important that radiographers understand that milliampere-seconds (mAs) is a setting that can be adjusted by the X-ray operator, and it has the greatest effect on patient dose. Recall that mAs = mA × s (exposure time). The mA value is the first component of mAs, and it determines the number of electrons that are accessible when the filament of the X-ray tube is heated. Once the heat applied to the filament intensifies, the production of electrons increases, which controls the amount of X-rays that are generated. The second component of mAs is the exposure length (in seconds). Typically, the exposure time is in milliseconds (ms) because most exposures are quicker than one second. Radiographers should understand that exposure to the patient and the amount of time the X-ray tube is on is a direct relationship. However, neither of these components can control the quantity of the exposure by themselves.

The relationship between mAs and receptor exposure is one that is directly proportionate. For example, if two exposures are taken, and the second one is three times as long, then it is assumed that three times as many X-rays are created during the second exposure. Recall that the current applied to the X-ray machine (mA) and the amount of exposure time (s) determine the mAs and, therefore, the intensity of the X-rays that interact with the image receptor. When the radiographer bumps up the mAs, the result is a greater quantity of electrons that move from the cathode to the anode within the X-ray tube, emitting more X-rays from the tube. In order to create an X-ray of acceptable exposure parameters, the radiographer must be sure that the technique chosen will be sufficient to allow enough X-rays to come into contact with the image receptor.

Radiographers are trained to know that mAs controls the amount of patient exposure and density of the X-ray image produced. Density is an older term used for what was once referred to as the overall "darkness" of an exposure. Today, this terminology is referred to as the receptor exposure, which still refers to the quantity of X-rays that have come into contact with the image receptor. Density is predominantly controlled by the mA setting, which is the rate at which current is applied, creating the number of electrons that are moving from the cathode to anode. When the radiographer increases the mA of an exposure, more X-rays are generated each second. When using a lower mA, the tube produces X-rays more slowly. If there aren't enough electrons available to pass from one end of the tube to the other, then there won't be enough X-ray photons created to reach the image receptor.

When considering the proper technique for a specific exam, the radiographer can adjust the main controls on the X-ray machine: the kilovolts peak (kVp) and the mAs (the product of mA × s). Either kVp or kV is used to refer to the energy or the speed of the electrons that move across the X-ray tube passing from the cathode to the anode end. When the kVp is increased, the electrons will move more rapidly and provide more energy. If the radiographer wishes to double the receptor exposure (density) of the film without changing the mAs, it is possible to do so by increasing the kVp by 15%. If a radiographer wants to halve the receptor exposure, the X-ray operator could decrease the kVp by 15%.

The kVp used during an X-ray exposure controls the energy or speed of the electrons as they pass through the X-ray tube. Therefore, kVp controls the quality of X-ray photons that will hit the image receptor. If the X-ray operator increases the kVp, then more electrons will be passed from one end of the X-ray tube to the other, resulting in more electrons reaching the anode. There is a direct relationship between kVp and the receptor exposure (density), but unlike the relationship between the mAs and the receptor exposure, it is not a proportionate correlation. Radiographers should be familiar with the 15% rule, which is a quick way to understand that the exposure receptor can be doubled by increasing the kVp by 15% (when the mAs remains the same). The receptor exposure can also be halved by decreasing the kVp by 15%.

The scale of contrast can be defined as the variation of brightness of structures that are visualized on a radiographic display. Grayscale may be categorized as demonstrating a long scale of contrast or a short scale of contrast. Images that are considered to have a long scale of contrast will illustrate many shades of gray, but the differences between the shades of gray are not extreme (low contrast). Images that are referred to as having a long scale of contrast are created when the kVp is higher. An example of a radiograph that has a long scale of contrast would be a kidney, ureter, and bladder (KUB) X-ray. Radiographic images that display a short scale of contrast tend to demonstrate structures that tend to be more black and white or have greater variations between the shades of gray (high contrast). These images are generated when a lower kVp setting is used. An example of a short scale of contrast would be a radiograph of the hand.

Kilovolts peak (kVp) is a common term used in radiography. This setting on the X-ray console is used primarily to control the penetrability and photon energy of the X-ray beam. A higher kVp setting is required when the tissue thickness and/or density of the part being examined increases as compared to smaller and/or lower density components within the body. It is important to remember that when radiographers use a higher kVp, then more scatter radiation will be produced. The ability of the X-ray photons to penetrate the patient, and the table will determine the number of X-rays that contact the image receptor to create an image. Sometimes, radiographers may use compression to reduce the thickness of a tissue. This reduction of tissue thickness will create less scatter, and the kVp can likely be reduced (which also creates less scatter). One example of a compression technique used is during mammography.

One of the most important reasons that a radiographer would want to use a higher kVp setting during a chest X-ray is to reduce the amount of radiation dose to the patient. Patients will often have several follow-up chest X-rays, and it is important to use the same technique so that the radiologist has comparable studies to read. The patient dose is reduced because when a higher kVp setting is used, then a lower mAs setting can be used. A radiograph demonstrates various structures that have different densities such as air and bone. A higher kVp setting will allow the visualization of pulmonary vascular markings as well as making the entire image more uniform. A longer scale of contrast is produced with increased kVp, which enables the ribs, sternum, and spine to be sufficiently penetrated.

Kilovolts peak (kVp) controls the energy and speed of the electrons as they pass from the cathode to the anode end of the tube. Therefore, kVp regulates the quality of the X-ray photons. When the X-ray operator increases the kVp, the speed of the electrons becomes faster, which increases the energy of the beam and allows for greater penetration of the X-rays. A lower kVp setting applies less voltage to the X-ray tube, which will result in less energy (less penetrating power) and a slower speed of the electrons as they are carried from the cathode to the anode. Radiographers should know that the mAs setting will control the quantity of X-ray photons that are generated during an X-ray. As the number of photons increases, the dose to the patient also increases, which makes mAs the primary controller of patient dose.

Radiographic contrast can be defined as the variability of brightness that can be discerned on the image display. If a radiograph displays several shades of gray between black and white, then it is considered to have a long scale of contrast, but the difference between the shades of gray tends to be minimal. Radiographs with a long scale of contrast are created by using a higher kVp setting. Due to many shades of gray being present in this example, the resultant contrast on the image will be low. Conversely, when a lower kVp setting is used, there will be a shorter scale of contrast because fewer gray tones are present. The image will demonstrate structures that have a more black-and-white appearance, which is considered to be high contrast.

Recall that the object to image receptor distance (OID) is the gap that separates the anatomical structure being examined and the image receptor. Radiographers should be aware of the OID at all times because an OID that is erroneously large can create an image that is magnified. If an image is larger than it should be, the image resolution may suffer. This can be detrimental because a radiologist may miss a fracture if the radiograph does not demonstrate the correct amount of detail. To prevent the loss of detail, radiographers should always use the smallest obtainable OID. A lateral chest X-ray will display a small amount of magnification of the heart, but one way that radiographers can overcome a large amount of magnification is to have the left side of the patient closest to the image receptor because the heart is on the left side.

The use of grids is a great way to decrease the amount of scatter radiation that contacts the image receptor. However, the use of grids requires a higher technique, which results in more exposure to the patient. The air gap method can be used for some exams so that the use of a grid is not necessary. When using an air gap technique, the radiographer positions the patient so that the OID is greater. This increase in OID is also allows magnification of the image, which was the main way to do so before digital imaging. A common radiograph that uses the air gap method is a lateral cervical spine X-ray. Due to the shoulders being in the way, the neck is not able to be placed right next to the image receptor, but the patient should be as close to the image receptor as possible so that the image is not overly magnified.

The inverse square law compares the intensity of the X-ray beam and the source to image distance (SID). Recall that the SID is the distance, often measured in inches, that separates the X-ray tube and the image receptor. The inverse square law implies that the intensity of the beam is inversely proportional to the square of the SID. The difference of the intensity across the X-ray beam is due to the divergence of the X-ray photons as it leaves the tube housing and travels toward the image receptor. The new intensity or distance can be determined by entering the known values in this formula:

$$\frac{I_1}{I_2} = \frac{D_2^2}{D_1^2}$$

Radiographers should be familiar with the exposure maintenance formula. The exposure maintenance formula should be used to determine the new mAs when the source to image distance (SID) has changed. If the SID is increased by a factor of two, then the radiographer must also increase the mAs (by a factor of four). This is an important concept for radiographers to remember, for example, when performing a chest X-ray on a patient in the ICU that is unable to sit upright because he or she is on a ventilator. The operator would not use the same mAs at 40 inches as would typically be used at 72 inches. The exposure maintenance formula can be applied when you have the original mAs to calculate the new mAs:

$$\frac{E_1}{E_2} = \frac{D_1^2}{D_2^2}$$

If a radiographer is performing an X-ray of the ankle, it is necessary to demonstrate as much detail as possible. A small focal spot should be chosen whenever possible to generate more detail and sharpness of the structure being examined. In the X-ray of the ankle in this example, one would want to visualize the soft tissue as well as the bony trabecular pattern of the bone. The focal spot size is predetermined by X-ray manufacturers based on the mA that is chosen during an exam. Typically, if using an mA of 200 or less, a small focal spot size will be programmed into the machine. A focal spot size of 0.3 mm or less may be chosen when a large OID is selected such as when a structure requires magnification. When magnification radiography is used, the amount of penumbra increases, so using a fractional focal spot (less than 0.3 mm) is a great way to decrease the amount of image blur.

Recall that a grid is used in almost every case that involves the patient's trunk. Grids are used to reduce the amount of primary and scattered radiation while allowing the remnant radiation to continue in the direction of the image receptor. The grid ratio is the comparison of how tall the lead strips are to the spacing between them. Grids that have a higher grid ratio will absorb more unnecessary X-ray photons. When using a grid, the receptor exposure will be lower unless the radiographer adjusts for the reduction of scatter. An increase of tissue thickness causes an increase in the amount of scattering, which also increases the amount of fog on a radiograph. Radiographers should remember that the patient is where the majority of scatter radiation is produced.

Recall that a grid will be used to reduce the number of scattered photons that strike the image receptor. When a grid is used, the lead strips within tend to absorb the scattered photons, which indicates that less fog will be present on the image. This creates an image that is categorized as high contrast because there will be fewer shades of gray due to the reduction in the fog. If a grid is not used, especially in cases in which the tissue being examined is greater than 10–12 cm, there will be more shades of gray because more scattered photons were enabled to reach the image receptor. This would be categorized as a short scale of contrast because the eyes will see many shades of gray even if there are small differences among them.

The main purpose of filtration during radiography procedures is to protect the patient (and radiology personnel) from unnecessary radiation exposure. The X-ray beam is considered to be a heterogeneous wave, which refers to the wide variation of wavelengths that the photons within possess. Those photons that demonstrate long wavelengths are more concerning when considering patient exposure because they do not have the required energy to pass through the patient and continue to the image receptor (IR). However, if the X-ray manufacturers did not include filtration devices to absorb this type of radiation, then the patient would end up absorbing this radiation, which would remarkably increase the patient's dose. Examples of inherent (built-in) filtration include the tube housing as well as the oil that surrounds the tube, and it is about 0.5 mm Al equivalent.

Filtration is an important device that is used to absorb the low-energy photons that are not strong enough to pass through the patient to create an image. However, it is still important to remove these low-energy photons so they do not find their way into the patient's body. If this takes place, it will increase the radiation dose to the patient. If more filtration is added, the result is an X-ray beam that has fewer of the long-wavelength X-rays that tend to find their way into the patient. The X-ray beam will possess a shorter wavelength (the radiation in this case is often referred to as a hard beam). These photons are more efficient because they do have the ability to strike the image receptor to create an image. Filtration is inversely related to contrast: As more filtration is added between the source and the patient, the amount of contrast will decrease.

Beam restriction (otherwise known as collimation) allows the radiographer to reduce the size of the X-ray beam. This is an important adjustment to make when performing an X-ray exam because it can limit the radiation that the patient is exposed to. For example, when performing lumbar spine X-rays, the X-ray operator must collimate because the tissues lateral to the spine do not need to be irradiated. When a radiographer minimizes the amount of tissue that is exposed to radiation, the receptor exposure decreases. When the size of the beam is restricted (increased collimation), less scatter radiation will be generated, which will also reduce the amount of receptor exposure (radiographic density decreases). When there is less scatter, there will also be less fog to reach the image receptor. Scatter radiation is primarily controlled with beam restriction.

Recall that collimation is also referred to as beam restriction. This functionality of the collimation device will allow radiographers to reduce the size of the X-ray beam. This is extremely important so that the anatomical structures that are adjacent to those in question are not also irradiated and, therefore, a smaller amount of tissue radiation occurs. Collimation tends to increase contrast due to less scatter being generated. When scatter is present, it contributes to the amount of fog, which will generally increase the shades of gray that are visible on the X-ray. However, when collimation is properly performed, there will be less scatter with a reduction of those gray shades, which increases contrast. The number of Compton interactions that occur in the body is reduced by using beam restriction.

Radiographers must consider the anode heel effect when using a large image receptor. When choosing a large image receptor, the X-ray beam is being used in its entirety. There will be a variation of X-ray intensity within the longitudinal axis of the beam. This intensity tends to be greater at the cathode end of the radiation field, and it tends to be less toward the anode end. Therefore, when performing an anteroposterior (AP) thoracic spine X-ray or an exam of the femur, it is important to know which end of the tube is the anode because the body part that is thinner will be directed underneath. In these examples, the patient's neck and the distal end of the femur should be under the anode. The thicker portions of the patient will be placed under the cathode and, in the aforementioned examples, the inferior portion of the thoracic spine and the proximal portion of the femur. If the anode heel effect is not considered, the thinner portions will appear overexposed on the image. If the anode and cathode are not clearly marked, the anode has a positive (+) charge and the cathode has a negative (–) charge and may be marked as such.

Shape distortion is a falsification of the shape of the anatomical structure of interest on an X-ray image. Elongation and foreshortening are two forms of shape distortion that may be present during a radiographic exam. Elongation occurs when the tube or the image receptor is not aligned correctly with the anatomical structure of interest. Improper angulation of the tube along the axis, for example, can make a bone look longer than it really is. The opposite of elongation is foreshortening, which, as the name implies, causes a body part to look shorter than it actually is. This is the result of angulation of the tube against the main axis of the bone when the tube, body part, or image receptor is not aligned correctly. Radiographers should realize that due to their normal position, some parts of the body will appear distorted, but it is not due to improper tube angulation or alignment.

Technique Charts

Anatomically Programmed Technique and Caliper Measurement

Every radiology department should have a technique chart to serve as a guide concerning the exposure factors for exams that will be performed. These technique charts are often based on the size of the patient, but the radiographer must also consider the SID, the image receptor, and whether a grid is required (including grid factors). A good way to start a technique chart is to measure the part thickness of the patient with a caliper. A caliper is a tool that has an adjustable "jaw" that can provide measurements in inches or centimeters. It is important that both parts of the caliper are in contact with the patient but are not compressing the tissues too much because inaccuracies may lead to settings that cause under- or overexposure. The tissue thickness can be recorded along with acceptable exposure techniques used to generate an acceptable image. Measuring the part thickness with a caliper is a great way for radiology students, new technologists, or new employees to learn the equipment to reduce the amount of unnecessary exposures.

Fixed Versus Variable kVp

The variable-kVp method is used when a specific mAs has already been allocated to every projection of the anatomical structures to be examined. Two to three kVp is added when there is an increase of 1 cm of patient thickness. The basis behind variable-kVp charts is to assume that thicker portions of the body require more penetration. Variable-kVp charts may allow for more image detail because the overall contrast of the image will be lower. It is important to measure the patient with a caliper if using a variable-kVp chart so that an increase in patient thickness is obvious and to create proper comparison radiographs when necessary. A fixed-kVp chart will require a specific kVp for the body part that is being examined, and the mAs is adjusted for patient thickness.

Special Considerations

Casts

Two main types of materials are used to make casts when a patient has fractured a bone. Casts are a type of support system that encases the entire portion of the bone so that it can heal correctly. If a reduction is required, a physician may choose a plaster cast because it tends to provide a better matrix to hold a bone in place, especially when the bone had to be put back into place. The disadvantage of using plaster is that it tends to be uncomfortable for the patient because it is heavy and cannot get wet because it can change shape, affecting the efficiency of healing. Techniques must be adjusted when an X-ray is required, and if the patient presents for an X-ray with a plaster cast that is wet it, this will require the operator to increase the exposure by three times. A dry plaster cast may only need twice the mAs. Fiberglass casts are typically used when reduction is not required. These casts tend to be lower maintenance because they can be worn longer, breathe more, are lighter, and come in various colors. A fiberglass cast doesn't typically require an increase of exposure when it is dry.

Pathologic Factors

Osteoporosis is a common pathologic condition that radiographers will encounter when obtaining a patient's history. Osteoporosis is caused by a loss of bone density, which creates bones that are porous (imagine a bone that is similar to a sponge). This weakening of the bones puts the individual at an increased risk of bone fractures. Common locations of skeletal fractures due to osteoporosis include the hip, wrist, and spine. Osteoporosis is often seen in the elderly (especially female patients), those that have inadequate calcium and vitamin D, and smokers. If a patient discloses that he or she has osteoporosis, the radiographer should decrease the amount of exposure because of the loss of density. Less kVp can be used because this controls the penetrability of the X-ray beam, and much less energy will be required to penetrate bones that are weaker.

Automatic Exposure Control (AEC)

Effects of Changing Exposure Factors on Radiographic Quality

The purpose of using automatic exposure control (AEC) when performing X-ray exams is to provide a high-quality radiograph that can be replicated when follow-up comparison studies are required. The use of AEC requires an advanced understanding of anatomy, expertise in patient positioning, recognition of the location of the ionization chambers, and an awareness of which sensors to use during exams. The ionization chambers are positioned between the anatomical structure and the image receptor, but it is up to the operator to determine which chambers are necessary in order to make a high-quality exposure. The radiographer must then place the body part over the selected chamber and ensure that the proper kVp is chosen to generate the desired contrast. The mAs is determined by the mA station that is selected and the seconds (s) or length of the exposure. Once the correct quantity of radiation has interacted with the radiation detector, the exposure is discontinued.

AEC allows X-ray operators to change the kVp as needed while the X-ray unit determines the necessary mAs. Recall that kVp controls the quality of the X-ray photons that come into contract with the image receptor. The kVp controls the energy or the penetrability of the beam, so when the radiographer adjusts the kVp, the exposure may become a shorter or longer scale of contrast. Adjusting the kVp will not affect the receptor exposure or how dark the image becomes, but modifications will take place regarding the contrast when changing the kVp. A higher kVp will demonstrate more shades of gray (lower contrast) to the eyes. A lower kVp will display an image that shows more black and white (higher contrast).

Detector Selection

Manufacturers offer AEC with two main features of the equipment selected. The type of AEC used in older equipment consists of what is referred to as a phototimer. These photomultiplier tubes are positioned behind the patient and the fluorescent screen, and they determine when the proper exposure has been reached. An ionization chamber is used in digital imaging, and it is positioned between the patient and the image receptor; it contains dry air that becomes ionized when enough radiation reaches the chamber, which terminates the exposure. Three detectors are available in both of the aforementioned controls. Selection of these sensors will depend on the exam being performed and the size of the image receptor. For example, the X-ray operator may choose only one sensor when performing an exam of the spine. More than one sensor may be necessary when performing chest or abdominal radiographs.

Anatomical Alignment

When a radiographer uses AEC, the machine will stop the exposure when enough radiation has interacted with the image detector. The X-ray operator sets the kVp for the anatomical structure of interest, while allowing the machine to "pull" the right amount of mAs. The radiographer must know the location of the detectors so that the body part is positioned in the correct location because different combinations of sensors can be used. For example, when performing an AP projection of the knee, the operator will only choose the middle sensor but must have the knee aligned directly over the sensor or the machine will be detecting the wrong portion of the body. The kVp setting also depends on the structures of the body being examined, so the radiographer must be sure to choose the correct cell and kVp to obtain the desired gray-scale image.

Exposure Adjustment

Recall that AEC enables the radiographer to choose the kVp, so the end result is an image that has the correct gray scale while the machine automatically determines the receptor exposure. When the kVp is adjusted, it enables the X-ray operator to obtain the correct contrast because it is determined by the energy of the X-ray beam. The radiographer can quickly adjust the density or receptor exposure when using the automatic exposure control by pressing the +1 or –1 button on the console, which is especially helpful in situations that require a repeat exposure. When the +1 function is used, it usually increases the density by 25%. When the –1 is chosen, the receptor exposure or density is reduced by 25%. When the operator must repeat an X-ray due to incorrect density, he or she must adjust the mAs by 30% or more.

Digital Imaging Characteristics

Spatial Resolution (Equipment Related)

Spatial resolution refers to the amount of detail that is visualized in an image. This detail includes the sharpness of an image and whether or not it is blurry. When spatial resolution is optimized, the edges are shown in great detail. Spatial resolution is also known as image resolution, definition, sharpness, and detail. The size of the focal spot is the component of the X-ray system that controls the amount of spatial resolution. In particular, a small focal spot is responsible for an increase of spatial resolution or detail. Although the focal spot size cannot always be adjusted by the radiographer, a small focal spot should be chosen when increased detail is desired. The focal spot size is often determined by the mA selection on the X-ray machine, and lower mA settings typically use a small focal spot.

Pixel Characteristics

An image acquired in a digital radiograph is stored in a pixel, which is also referred to as a picture element. These tiny picture elements are the smallest units of the matrix that display a shade of gray that correlates with anatomical tissue of the patient that is being imaged. When combined, these shades of gray create the digital X-ray. Pixels are two dimensional and represent the *x* and *y* axes. When a third dimension, *z*, is measured, it is known as a voxel, or volume element, and it represents the depth. There is an inverse relationship between pixel size and resolution. The image resolution tends to increase with a smaller pixel size. For example, if a matrix is larger, there will be more pixels, but they will be smaller. This scenario creates an image with increased resolution.

Matrix Size

A digital radiograph is a matrix that is determined by the total number of pixels (picture elements). The matrix size is decided by the quantity of pixels that are aligned in columns and rows (*x* and *y* planes). Field of view (FOV) is a common term used in radiography, and it describes how much of the anatomical area of interest is involved in the matrix. The matrix and FOV can be altered separately without influencing each other, but either of these actions will affect the pixel size. If the matrix size is large, more pixels will be present (although they will be smaller in size) thus increasing the resolution. If the matrix size is smaller, there will be fewer pixels, and their large size will create a mosaic appearance, which decreases the resolution.

Contrast Resolution (Equipment Related)

Bit Depth

In radiography, bit depth refers to the depth of the picture element (pixel). Recall that pixels are a two-dimensional components of an image that correlate a shade of gray to a specific anatomical tissue of a patient within the matrix. The number of shades of gray that a pixel can demonstrate is controlled by the bit depth. Bit depth is determined by the X-ray manufacturer based on the various exams that can be performed by this specific piece of equipment. The capability of an X-ray system to recognize minute changes in exposure due to tissue differences is the definition of contrast resolution. If the bit depth is smaller, there won't be as many shades of gray possible within the image. However, if the pixel contains more bits, the bit depth is bigger, and more shades of gray can be demonstrated within the image.

Modulation Transfer Function (MTF)

The modulation transfer function (MTF) is the term used to describe the amount of contrast resolution that the X-ray system as a whole can generate. The MTF of a general imaging system compares the contrast of the image to the actual contrast of the object that is being examined. The MTF is expressed in numbers ranging from 0 to 1. If the MTF of the X-ray unit is 1, it means that the contrast resolution of the image has not been attenuated at all and has an MTF of 100%. Because the MTF evaluates the contrast and spatial resolution, it also represents the amount of imaging detail, or the amount of blur that is present in the X-ray image in a particular range of spatial frequencies. These capabilities of the MTF make it an effective function of the system that evaluates the true resolution.

Image Signal (Exposure Related)

Dynamic Range

Dynamic range is a ratio of X-ray exposures that will generate an acceptable image, and it measures the response of a detector when it is exposed to X-rays. The intrinsic noise of the X-ray unit will govern the minimum intensity that can be generated. The dynamic range in digital radiography tends to be wider than what screen film offers. A wide dynamic range is advantageous because an image can display various types of tissue on one radiograph. A wide dynamic range may also reduce the amount of radiation exposure to the patient, but care must still be taken when the radiographer is selecting the exposure technique for the anatomical part being examined. Conventional film-screen radiography has a dynamic range that tends to take on an S-shaped curve, and the image quality will be degraded when the exposure does not fall within this already narrow exposure window. The wider exposure latitude is just one advantage of digital radiography.

Quantum Noise (Quantum Mottle)

Digital imaging does not exclude radiographers from grasping the principles of X-ray physics. When conventional X-ray exams are performed, if the correct techniques were not chosen, the X-ray operator had to repeat the exposure(s) while keeping the as low as reasonably achievable (ALARA) principle in mind. Technologists that use digital imaging systems must also follow the ALARA principle, although sometimes a repeat exposure may be avoided if the image can be "windowed" to achieve an image that provides diagnostic value. However, quantum mottle or noise may affect the image if the wrong techniques are selected. In this case, no amount of "windowing" can correct the image because not enough X-ray photons reached the image receptor. This could be from a kVp (or mAs) setting that is too low. Unlike conventional radiography, digital radiography is especially susceptible to this noise, which creates an image that appears grainy.

Signal-to-Noise Ratio (SNR)

Digital radiography will always be subjected to noise (which could be electronic or quantum mottle) when generating an image. The effect of this noise on the resultant image is known as the signal-to-noise ratio (SNR). Signal designates the information that is actually useful in the creation of an image. Noise refers to the data that do not contribute to the creation of the image. If an image has more signal than noise, it is deemed to be of higher quality than one that displays more noise than signal. A high SNR will generate less noise on the image in order to produce an X-ray image of high diagnostic quality. Manufacturers work to create images that provide the most spatial resolution by reducing the amount of noise that is generated when the pixel size decreases.

Image Identification

Methods

Once an image has been taken and prior to submission to the radiologist, the technologist must be sure that the patient's information can be read and that it contains all pertinent identifiers. These identifiers include the name and date of birth of the individual, the date that the exam was performed, the name of the facility at which the X-ray was taken, as well as the patient identification number, which is a unique number generated for each patient. Another important step to perform before sending the exam to the radiologist is to make sure that the side is properly marked and the lead marker is visible. Often, facilities will require their technologists to use lead markers prior to the exposure that contain their initials so that it is known which technologist performed the exam. These lead markers are also used to mark the side of the patient on the image. Often, additional annotations may be necessary and can be added after the image has been taken. These should not obscure any anatomy and must also be correct; examples of these annotations include weight bearing, flexion, or extension.

Legal Considerations

Patients that have radiographic procedures, whether performed in a hospital or in an outpatient setting, are protected by the Health Insurance Portability and Accountability Act (HIPAA). This act was introduced in 1996 to protect the health information of patients and is a national standard set forth by the US Department of Health and Human Services. When patients report for an exam, a HIPAA form will be presented to be signed. This form educates individuals of their rights for privacy and security. Radiographers must be certain to not share information about a patient whether it is the specifics of the exam that was performed or the results with anybody that does not need to know. For example, if a respected surgeon reports to the X-ray department for a chest X-ray because of hemoptysis, the radiographer must not share with the hospital staff that he or she was seen and that a tumor was found (if the results are positive). Patient information should not be accessed unless necessary because this is a serious offense and can be tracked in the electronic medical record system via sign-on credentials.

Criteria for Image Evaluation of Technical Factors

Exposure Indicator

For radiographers who have used conventional X-ray equipment, it was apparent once the film came out of the processor if the correct exposure technique was selected. If the film was too dark, it was overexposed. If the structures appeared too light, it would need to be repeated at a higher exposure setting. However, with digital images, it may not be as obvious if the correct exposure factors were not selected. The radiographer should always check the exposure indicator (EI) to determine if the techniques are within the acceptable range for the exam being performed. Depending on the manufacturer of the X-ray unit, the EI may have various names, and for facilities that have equipment from more than one vendor, it is important the staff are familiar with all of them (S-number, Exl, and REG are just a few examples).

Image Artifacts

Conventional X-ray films were susceptible to many types of image artifacts. Recall that artifacts are unforeseen errors in imaging, and they are a common cause for repeat exposures. These artifacts could stem from problems of the cassette, dirt or foreign bodies on the intensifying screens, bending of the X-ray film during handling, or a number of issues from the processor. Great care is required when handling X-ray cassettes because they are prone to cracks, especially when dropped. These cracks can create light leaks that can obstruct the anatomy on the image. Radiographers also have to make sure that the film is not bent as the film is being loaded into the cassette or into the developer. The film processor can also be a source of artifacts because rollers that are not moving correctly can leave scratch marks on the film. The temperature of the processor must be evaluated, and care must be taken when adding developer and/or fixer so that the chemicals do not contaminate the other tanks.

A moiré pattern is an artifact that gives the appearance of wavy lines throughout the image after acquisition takes place. This artifact is the result of the grid being fed into the reader of a CR system when the grid lines are parallel to the scanning lines. Recall that the reader removes the imaging plate from the cassette and scans it with a laser beam, which will energize the photons that are embedded in the plate. To avoid a moiré pattern on the image, the grid lines must be fed into the reader so they are perpendicular to the laser lines of the reader. This can be avoided by using a moving grid because the grid lines are automatically blurred. Also, many vendors recommend using grids with frequencies of more than 150 lines/in to reduce the chances of this artifact.

Radiation Fog

Fog can be defined as an accidental exposure to the image receptor that will negatively affect the quality of the X-ray image. If films are left in the exam rooms while other exposures are being made, the scatter radiation could fog the film (radiation fog). The result of fog tends to be an observed density that is higher than expected. In exams that should demonstrate high contrast, the objects that typically appear bright white tend to take on a grayer appearance. Fog is often the result of scatter radiation, but in conventional radiography there are other types of fog as well. These are often the result of using improper film storage or processing procedures. Examples of improper processing procedure include a prolonged exposure to the safelight that is located in the darkroom or a bulb that is too bright (safelight fog). During processing, an increased temperature of the developer may create temperature fog.

Equipment Operation and Quality Assurance

Imaging Equipment

X-Ray Generator, Transformers, and Rectification System

Basic Principles

Transformers are responsible for the high voltages that the X-ray equipment needs to produce an image. One of the components of the X-ray circuit is an autotransformer (also known as a variable transformer), which provides power to the other portions of the circuit. However, the most important function of the autotransformer is to allow the radiographer to choose the correct kVp setting, which will depend on the anatomical part that is being evaluated by sending more voltage to the high-voltage transformer. The autotransformer is one coiled wire that enables the voltage to increase when it is sent to the primary side of the step-up transformer. An autotransformer needs AC to function and is found on the low-voltage side of the X-ray circuit. Keep in mind that the prefix "auto" means self, and the autotransformer runs because of self-induction.

The rectifier (also referred to as a solid-state diode) is the component of the radiographic unit that changes the type of current from alternating current (AC) into direct current (DC). AC power is supplied from the company that provides power to the facility, but the X-ray tube must have DC power. The rectifier is positioned between the step-up transformer, which operates on AC, and the X-ray tube (as mentioned earlier, it functions on DC power). DC is preferred for digital imaging because a constant power supply is available, which offers a more consistent supply of X-rays. In contrast to AC, DC cannot change directions and the intensity is not altered.

Phase, Pulse, and Frequency

Most digital radiographic units that are being used today operate with a high-frequency generator. X-ray manufacturers recognized the value of demonstrating a nearly constant voltage potential as those that were being generated in portable X-ray units (which were one of the first systems to use high-frequency generators along with mammography units). This increase of voltage that is offered not only boosts the quantity of the X-ray photons, but it also improves the quality of the X-ray images. In addition, not only are these generators smaller in size, but they have also proven to reduce the amount of radiation to the patient during an exam because fewer low-energy photons are present. These low-energy photons do not have enough energy to pass through the patient and end up being absorbed by the body. The high-frequency generator has a range of 500–25,000 Hz and has very little ripple (roughly 1%).

Tube Loading

When radiographers select an exposure technique for an image, the falling-load generator determines the best way for the equipment to obtain the particular mAs that was chosen by the operator. When the exposure first begins, the X-ray tube is at a maximum level until the tube reaches the highest heat load for the mA setting that was chosen. At this point, the falling-load generator will keep switching to a lower mA station that will allow the mAs to be obtained by using an exposure time that is as quick as possible. Radiographers may choose to use breathing techniques for some exams (such as a lateral thoracic spine to blur the lungs), which lengthens the time of the exposure as well as heating of the tube. More heat also increases within the tube when back-to-back exposures are made.

Components of the Radiographic Unit (Fixed or Mobile)

Operating Console

The operating console for digital radiographic units typically consists of buttons allowing the radiographer to choose the correct settings for the exam to be performed. These buttons will enable the technologist to control the kVp, mA, seconds (length of the exposure), as well as select the size of the focal spot. When the patient has been properly positioned and the correct technique has been set, there is also a rotor and exposure switch on the console. Every manufacturer must also provide a digital readout so that once an exposure has been taken, the technologist knows how much exposure was required. Manufacturers will also preprogram exposure settings; therefore, the radiographer may choose a button that represents a certain anatomical part (for example, the hand). There will typically be settings in the machine for the various projections to be performed so that the technologist can complete every exam as quickly as possible. To protect the employees from scatter radiation, these controls are within an area that is separated from the exam room by a lead barrier.

X-Ray Tube Construction: Electron Source

When high-speed electrons are transmitted from the filament of the cathode end of the X-ray tube and slow down once they contact the target of the anode end, X-rays are generated. Two methods that enable the production of X-rays are bremsstrahlung (brems) radiation and characteristic radiation. Brems radiation accounts for the majority of the X-ray photons within the beam (70%–90%). Brems radiation is also referred to as braking radiation because as the incoming negatively charged electron moves toward the nucleus of the target atom in the anode, it decelerates, or brakes. The X-ray photon is released as the result of the decrease of energy of the incident electron. The other method of radiation production is characteristic radiation. This takes place if an incoming electron hits a K shell tungsten electron causing it to be ejected from the inner shell. An L or M shell electron must fill the hole in the K shell, and as that electron drops into the K shell, energy is released as an X-ray photon. These electrons are forced to shift until the atom is stable. Characteristic X-rays occur when the radiographer chooses a setting higher than 70 kVp and forms about 15% of the beam.

X-Ray Tube Construction: Target Materials

The target is the area in which the X-rays are created as the electrons move from the cathode to the anode end of the X-ray tube. The target is comprised of a molybdenum disk that is surrounded by tungsten. Tungsten is preferred because it has a high melting point due its high atomic number. The target of the X-ray tube is located on the anode (positive) side of the tube and has an angled (20 degrees or less) surface so that the electrons are more likely to come into contact with the anode. This area of the anode is known as the focal spot; a small focal spot offers more detail in the image because a lower temperature can be obtained. This explains why a small focal spot is chosen when more detail is desired; this is the effective focal spot, and it is a vertical representation of the focal spot in comparison to the image receptor. Higher temperatures will require the use of a larger focal spot due to the greater X-ray output that must be generated; this describes the actual focal spot because the electron stream hits the target here.

Recall from physics lessons that electrons have a negative charge. The X-ray tube is made of glass (Pyrex), and it holds the electron source (the cathode end) and the target (the anode end, which has a positive charge). It is a vacuum tube, so that the production of X-rays is not compromised by any gaseous molecules within. On the cathode end of the X-ray tube is a filament (electron source) that is comprised of wire made out of tungsten. Thermionic emission takes place when the X-ray operator starts the rotor on the machine. The cathode assembly of the X-ray tube is negatively charged because the positively charged anode attracts the negatively charged electrons, creating what is known as an electron stream. Once they interact with the target, most of the energy becomes heat (more than 99%) whereas only a small portion is converted into X-rays (less than 1%).

X-Ray Tube Construction: Induction Motor

The purpose of an induction motor is to extend the life of the X-ray tube for as long as possible. The induction motor controls the rotation of the anode, but it is actually located externally to the anode and is attached to a rotor. The anode is the target that is found within the X-ray tube and is the location at which X-rays are produced. Less than 1% of the energy is converted to X-rays; the rest of the energy generates heat. Due to the extreme temperatures, the induction motor enables the rotor to spin ranging from 3,300 to 10,000 rpm in order to dissipate some of the heat. Normally, the anode could rotate for up to 30 minutes after activation, but the induction motor is also responsible for stopping this rotation of the target. The ready switch that activates the rotor permits the rotor to reach the correct amount of revolutions per minute before an exposure is made. Often, the control panel will alert the technologist when to press the exposure button.

AEC

The radiographer must determine before an exposure is made if he or she will use AEC. This function of the X-ray system is not always on, but it is available with the touch of a button on the control panel. When it is engaged, the X-ray operator will be able to select the sensors to be used during the exam. Various combinations of detectors may be used depending on the anatomical part to be radiographed. For example, only the center cell may be selected if the radiographer wishes to use AEC during a knee X-ray, but he or she may need to choose all three when performing a KUB X-ray. Exams that require a free-standing grid cannot use the AEC function because detectors are not located in this type of image receptor. The radiographer must always set the kVp (fixed kVp) and a backup time to end the exposure should there be an AEC glitch.

Radiographers should always obtain a thorough patient history before starting an exam. This is especially true when the anatomical part being examined is covered up and the technologist is not able to see evidence from prior surgeries such as scars. Another important step that should be taken whenever possible is to check for prior X-rays and/or reports, especially for follow-up exams. When using the AEC function, is it imperative that the part being examined is centered over the correct sensors in order to optimize the image quality. If the patient has a prosthesis (or any metal screws or plates), the radiographer should not use AEC because it may create an image that is too dark. The reason that the exposure will likely take longer than it should is due to the hardware actually absorbing the radiation. Instead of directing the radiation toward the ionization chamber as it normally would without any hardware, absorption of the radiation fails to terminate the exposure as quickly as it should.

AEC: Radiation Detectors

AEC is a function of the X-ray system that enables radiographers to provide an image that displays the correct density. The use of AEC is also a way of providing consistency when follow-up exams are required because the exposure is turned off once enough radiation reaches the detector. In digital imaging, the radiation detector is positioned between the patient and the image receptor. This ionization chamber is wired to the electronic timer, and it consists of cells that are air filled. Once enough of the exit radiation from the patient ionizes these chambers, the timer will be signaled to terminate the exposure. A backup timer must be set in case the system malfunctions so that the exposure does not continue. Patient positioning is an essential part of the correct use of AEC. The body part must be centered over the correct detector(s) to generate a quality image.

AEC: Backup Timer

When a radiographer chooses to use AEC during an exposure, he or she must still set the correct kVp and choose the mA for that particular exam and patient size. AEC will determine how long the exposure should be so the image has the desired density. Another way to state this is that AEC controls the time (or seconds) that the X-ray beam is on. AEC works on the principle that the exposure will turn off once the image receptor has received the correct amount of radiation. AEC can often be useful for radiographers that are unsure of how much mAs an exam will require, but correct positioning of the anatomical part must be obtained with regard to the sensors that are chosen. AEC is beneficial for students and/or new personnel that are not yet familiar with the equipment because a readout of the mAs that is pulled will help for future exams. All equipment can malfunction, so a backup timer must be set when using AEC in order to discontinue the exposure if a defect occurs.

AEC: Minimum Response Time

Minimum response time (also referred to as minimum reaction time) is a principle that applies to an exam in which AEC is engaged. Recall that when AEC is being used, the time of the exposure is decided by the X-ray unit so that the radiographer does not have to select the mAs. The radiographer will choose the desired kVp and mA station, but the machine will turn off the exposure once enough radiation has arrived at the image receptor. The shortest length of time that it takes for the X-ray to be detected by the image receptor is known as the minimum response time. The shortest amount of time possible is 0.001 second (1 ms) when AEC is used. The radiographer must select a backup time in case of a mechanical defect of AEC in order to stop the exposure.

Manual Exposure Controls

Digital radiology equipment is similar to digital photography equipment in the sense that the operator may choose to use automatic or manual exposure techniques. Recall that the function of AEC is to determine the length of exposure by stopping it once enough radiation has reached the detectors. However, the radiographer must still set the kVp and select the mA station. This is similar to the automatic mode on a digital camera. However, if the operator chooses manual mode, then he or she has control over the kVp, mA, and length of exposure in seconds (s). Recall that mA and s equal mAs. The mA setting controls the quantity of photons (the seconds determines how long the exposure is on) that reach the image receptor, whereas the kVp setting controls the quality (penetrability) of the X-ray beam.

An exposure is made with the use of two buttons. The button that signals the anode to spin as well as heat the filament to start the thermionic emission process is the prep, standby, or ready switch. The exposure button will take the exposure, and modern equipment will prevent an exposure before the anode is spinning fast enough.

Beam Restriction

Radiographers must always practice proper beam restriction (collimation) of the X-ray beam in order to limit the amount of exposure that a patient receives. Proper collimation will protect adjacent tissue from radiation exposure because it limits the field of view in which the X-ray beam is directed. Not only does collimation limit the amount of exposure to the patient, but it also increases the image quality. For example, if an AP projection of the thoracic spine is desired while using the AEC function, the radiographer must collimate to the spine. If no beam restriction is applied, the resultant image will appear underexposed because of an increased amount of scatter that strikes the image receptor causing the exposure to be interrupted too quickly. The image contrast will also be degraded due to the scatter radiation.

Computed Radiography (CR) Components

Computed radiography (CR) requires the use of cassettes in order to create an image. The cassettes are similar in size to those that are used in film/screen (conventional) radiography. Instead of housing X-ray film and an intensifying screen, the active layer is a phosphor. The imaging plate has many components including a plastic covering that protects the phosphor. The active layer is made up of photostimulable phosphors (PSPs) such as barium fluorohalide or bromohalide that can capture electrons when an image is taken. The electrons that are located in this PSP layer receive their energy from the remnant (exit) radiation and will remain here until the cassette is fed into the image reader. Although the image can remain on the imaging plate for several hours, it should be read within 8 hours of the exposure because roughly 25% of the latent image will fade.

If a department is upgrading their X-ray system from a conventional to a CR system, the radiographer should adjust the exposure factors to those that are used in a 200–400 film/screen system, although most exams do not require a dramatic change in the techniques used after this upgrade because the CR unit will imitate the same result that one would obtain using a conventional X-ray. In fact, the CR system can be altered to conform to almost any speed that was previously adopted within the department. As with any new system that is implemented, the techniques may need to be adjusted accordingly for any studies that are performed. Radiographers may find it helpful to document techniques that have worked well in the specific exam room until feeling absolutely comfortable with the new equipment.

In contrast to a conventional X-ray machine, a CR machine does not require the use of a darkroom or film processor. In lieu of a chemical processor, a cassette reader is used to extract the image from the imaging plate. The entire cassette is placed within the reader, but only the imaging plate is removed, and it is scanned with a laser that provides energy for the electrons that are located within the PSP with extra energy to break out and emit a blue light. A photomultiplier will send the light to a digitizer, which will delegate a brightness level to each pixel within the matrix. The pattern in which the laser scans the imaging plate is known as a raster pattern. Some readers can only hold one imaging plate at a time, whereas others will allow the operator to load more than one at a time.

Direct Radiography (DR) Image Receptors

The main advantage of choosing a direct radiography (DR) system over a CR unit is the processing speed in which the radiographer can see the image while demonstrating exams that have extremely high quality. The dynamic range offered by DR systems is also an advantage. DR systems use flat panel detectors that are wired directly to the workstation, which increases the efficiency of the image processing. CR systems require the radiographer to feed the cassettes into the image reader in order to convert the PSP analog information into an image that is digital. DR flat panels are either direct or indirect detectors. The direct detector takes the remnant radiation from the patient and changes it into an electrical charge. The indirect detector first has to change the remnant radiation into visible light and then into electrical charges that will become digital images. Disadvantages of DR are the initial cost of the equipment because it is more expensive than CR and some radiographers may tend to overexpose a patient in order to manipulate the data afterward.

Indirect conversion digital radiography systems will convert X-ray photons into light. This is done because the flat panel detector is coated on the outside with a phosphor that will absorb the X-ray photons that this layer comes into contact with and change them to light. This process of converting X-ray photons into visible light is known as scintillation. Cesium iodide and gadolinium oxysulfide are the two most common substances used in the phosphor screens of indirect systems. This light is then changed by photodiodes into electrons that will make up tiny picture elements that are eventually processed in the computer to compose an image. A direct conversion system will omit the scintillator step, which makes it even more efficient because the X-ray photon is converted to an electric signal that is immediately sent to the analog-to-digital converter.

Recall that the two types of digital radiography are direct and indirect conversion. The direct conversion process is considered as such because it is a one-step process in which the x-ray photons that leave the patient are automatically converted into electrons to produce the image. When using indirect conversion radiology equipment, there is an extra step known as the scintillation layer. With this added step, the x-ray photons that leave the patient are first changed to light photons in the scintillation layer and are then passed onto a photodiode that converts the light photons into an electric charge. The material within the photodiode layer is an element called amorphous silicon. From this layer, the electrons are then sent to the thin-film transistor detector where the x-ray image is formed.

Components of the Fluoroscopic Unit (Fixed or Mobile)

Image Receptors: Image Intensifier

Fluoroscopic exams are an advanced imaging technique that offer physicians a live view of anatomical structures within the body. In a nondigital fixed or mobile fluoroscopic unit, the image intensifier is used to convert X-rays into a dynamic image that can be visualized on a monitor during an exam. There are many parts of the image intensifier, including the input phosphor, which captures X-rays that leave the patient and transforms them into light. Next, the light reaches the photocathode and is released as electrons (proportional in number to the amount of light that contacted it). These electrons are directed toward the opposite end of the image intensifier in which the output phosphor is located. It is this structure that converts the energy into even more light than the photocathode produced and allows the human eye to see the image. A mobile fluoroscopy unit is referred to as a C-arm due to the shape that is formed between the image intensifier and the tube. These units are typically used for surgical cases.

Radiographers should be aware that fluoroscopy systems are designed so that the X-ray tube is located under the radiographic table. This is a different location when compared to overhead images, in which the tube is in front of the patient. The radiation will be directed through the table and then enter and exit the patient before contacting the input phosphor, which changes the energy into visible light. Next, the visible light will be directed toward the photocathode, which will release a proportional amount of electrons to those that hit it. These electrons will then be guided to the opposite side of the image intensifier to the output screen. This component of the fluoroscopy unit will change the energy back into light that can be seen, but at levels that are 50%–75% higher than those at the photocathode.

The image intensifier in digital fluoroscopy units has several advantages over its nondigital counterparts due to the flat panel image receptor. This design provides more postprocessing functions. Another advantage is less exposure to the patient because of the use of a pulsed X-ray beam instead of one that is on continuously. This pulsation of the beam also keeps the heat of the system as low as possible. Some facilities have eliminated the need for overhead X-rays because of the amount of detail that can be captured with digital fluoroscopy — also reducing the amount of radiation exposure to the patient and medical personnel that are in the exam room. The amount of resolution is better, which provides physicians with more confidence when examining smaller anatomical structures. The monitors used in digital fluoroscopy suites should be of high resolution to provide greater amounts of detail. Flat panels may magnify the structures that are being examined without compromising the amount of detail that is offered.

Viewing Systems

The capabilities of digital fluoroscopic units are similar to those of digital radiography because the images can be manipulated after the images have been captured (postprocessing capabilities). Many facilities have eliminated overhead X-rays because the image quality is far superior to that performed with conventional fluoroscopy. One of the reasons that the quality is so much better is the use of monitors that are high-resolution flat panels. The viewing capabilities with these monitors are better because millions of pixels are used to create high-definition images. These flat panel monitors offer images that have better contrast resolution with maximum brightness and expanded display areas, and they allow customization for the physicians that will be performing the exam.

Automatic Brightness Control (ABC)/Automatic Exposure Rate Control (AERC)

Automatic brightness control (ABC)/automatic exposure rate control (AERC) is an automated process in which the fluoroscopy unit detects the necessary kVp and mA and modifies these settings as needed. ABC/AERC is also referred to as automatic brightness stabilization and automatic gain control. Depending on the type of exam that is being performed, the mA in conventional fluoroscopic exams is typically set between 3 and 5 mA. Most fluoroscopy units run on the ABC principle, so the system will constantly adjust the brightness on the image by modifying the techniques in order to keep the brightness the same. The brightness will fluctuate with various thicknesses of the anatomical tissue or when a new patient is imaged, so the system is constantly adjusting to keep the same brightness throughout the procedure. Typically, this is accomplished by altering the kVp as necessary, but the mA may also be changed.

Magnification Mode

When magnification mode is used during a fluoroscopic procedure, the radiation dose to the patient is elevated. Magnification mode refers to the enlargement of the image, which can be achieved by either geometric or electronic means. Geometric magnification can occur if the source and/or receptor are moved in relationship to the patient. For example, if the X-ray tube is adjusted so that it is closer to the patient whereas the image receptor is moved away from the patient, the image will become magnified. Electronic magnification is possible with today's systems which may offer three to five magnification modes, each increasing the patient dose. Magnification can offer diagnostic value when used correctly, but if a small focal spot is not used, the image's spatial resolution will suffer. Postprocessing functions also allow the physician to magnify an image whether it is done by choosing a region of interest or magnifying the entire image. This, of course, will not increase the patient dose because the image has already been saved.

Table

A radiographic table that is used during fluoroscopic exams offers more than just a place for the patient to lie on during the exam. The tables used are capable of tilting so that a patient can be evaluated in the standing position at the start of exams such as during barium swallows and upper

GI studies. A footboard is attached at the end of the table so that the patient may stand on it. The table can then be lowered into the horizontal position to continue evaluating the patient while he or she is recumbent. These tables also enable users to move the tabletop into various positions during an exam in order to center the X-ray beam where necessary without having to physically move the patient for each image. Under the surface of the table is a device that acts as a cassette holder and contains a grid to help absorb scatter radiation to improve image detail. This movable grid is also referred to as a Bucky assembly.

Accessories

Stationary Grids

CR uses cassettes that appear similar to those used in conventional radiology departments. Just like some exams in conventional radiography require the use of a stationary grid (in cases of thicker anatomical regions), it is important to note if the imaging plate to be used is a high-resolution plate or a standard plate. This is important because high-resolution plates are typically used when greater spatial resolution is desired, such as during an X-ray of a hand or foot. CR imaging plates are extremely sensitive to the effects of scatter, so the radiographer must pay close attention to the grid frequency and ratio, and if it is a focused grid. The most commonly used grid in the radiology department is the focused grid, but they require an X-ray beam that is centered correctly and are only used for the SID that is specified. Parallel grids cannot be used for an SID that is less than 48 inches, but they offer more flexibility in the centering of the X-ray beam.

Bucky Assembly

CR uses cassettes that are similar to those used in departments that still have conventional X-ray machines. These cassettes exist in various sizes, but instead of containing X-ray film and an intensifying screen, they house a plate made of phosphor that is scanned by the digital reader so the image can be displayed on a monitor. Many exams require the patient to stand against the cassette holder or even to lie on the table, and the Bucky assembly can be adjusted for the height of the patient, or it can be moved along the length of the table. The Bucky assembly has two main purposes, the first of which is to hold the cassette in place because many exams are not performed via the tabletop. Another important function of the Bucky assembly is to function as a grid that engages a motor during the exposure that creates blurring of the grid lines so they do not appear on the X-ray image. The grid ratio of the Bucky assembly is typically 12:1 or 16:1.

Compensating Filters

Added filtration is an integral component of digital imaging equipment. Added filtration helps protect the patient by decreasing the dose with the elimination of the photons that are considered to be of low energy. Filtration material is positioned between the X-ray tube and the patient, and it typically consists of aluminum. Radiographers do not actually adjust the amount of added filtration; this is left up to radiation physicists because they are the professionals that are responsible for monitoring and testing the equipment to make sure it is producing the correct levels of radiation. Radiographers do, however, use compensating filters during exams, which may include various tissue thicknesses to produce an image that has a uniform density. These are often attached to the collimator or placed on or near the patient and include wedge, boomerang, or trough filters.

Image Processing and Display

Raw Data (Preprocessing)

Histogram

Photographers that use digital cameras can opt to display the histogram to help determine if the correct exposure factors have been used. Radiographers can also choose to display the histogram when using digital radiography equipment and will see a graph with lines of various heights.

Similar to digital cameras, a histogram on the radiology monitor is a graphic display of the intensity of the pixels and how they are appropriated during an X-ray. This information can help the radiographer determine if the proper technique was selected because the *x*-axis represents the amount of exposure, whereas the *y*-axis demonstrates the number of pixels for the exposure that was produced. Histograms tend to be fairly consistent for exams of the same anatomical location as long as the correct algorithm is chosen when the imaging plate is read. For CR equipment that uses a higher kVp, the histogram tends to be narrower than that of an exam that is exposed with a lower kVp (the histogram will appear wider).

Corrected Data for Processing

Edge Enhancement

Spatial frequency resolution refers to the amount of image sharpness and detail that are controlled by the size of the focal spot and OID. One of the advantages of digital imaging is the ability to adjust the amount of enhancement of the image when necessary. One such adjustment that may be made is referred to as edge enhancement, which helps the person viewing the image better delineate the edges of the structure without affecting the internal components of the anatomy. The edge of the structure is enhanced when a limited number of pixels around the edge of the structures are chosen to be part of the average of the signals obtained. Edge enhancement is useful during orthopedic imaging as well as viewing soft-tissue structures. Many radiology departments prefer that radiographers do not apply postprocessing filters before the image is sent to the picture archiving and communication system.

Smoothing

Smoothing is a type of postprocessing function that can be performed to improve the quality of the image by decreasing the amount of noise in the image. Recall that digital images are susceptible to noise, which can degrade the quality of the X-ray image taken. Smoothing is a method that can be used to reduce the noise that is demonstrated in an image, and because noise does not contribute to image quality it is helpful when it can be reduced. Smoothing can reduce the amount of high-frequency noise by averaging the frequency of each pixel that displays noise with those frequencies of pixels that are adjacent to or near the noisy pixels. Smoothing is also referred to as low-pass filtering, but because the image becomes blurred when the low-pass filter is applied, less detail is demonstrated. Smoothing may also function to even out the brightness of the image.

Postprocessing

Brightness

One of the advantages of digital imaging is the ability of the operator or the reading physician to manipulate the image. One of the most common reasons that an image is changed is to adjust either the brightness or the contrast of the X-ray. Often, this is performed while moving the computer mouse in a horizontal or vertical direction. Changing the brightness of the image will make the image appear lighter or darker on the monitor. This is a postprocessing function that will affect the entire image, and it is directly related to the window level (the midpoint of the recorded densities). The image will become brighter if the operator increases the window level. The entire image will become darker once the operator decreases the window level. The dose of the patient is still controlled by the mAs selected, but the brightness is not affected as it was in conventional exams. Most facilities request that the radiographer does not change the window level because the radiologist's monitor is of higher definition than the one in the exam room, and it is preferred that he or she alters the image from that workstation if necessary.

Contrast

It is important that radiographers always apply the ALARA principle when performing X-ray exams. Digital radiography requires the correct exposure techniques when performing an exam just as conventional X-ray does, but with digital imaging, kVp does not affect contrast; rather, it affects the penetrability of the beam. However, if enough X-ray photons have reached the image receptor, the image can be adjusted by the operator or radiologist to window the contrast and brightness to optimize the image. Recall that radiographic contrast refers to the ratio of black to white (grayscale) in an image, and it can be windowed with a computer mouse. The window width is the parameter that affects the radiographic contrast, and there is an inverse relationship between the two. For example, as the window width becomes larger, the image will display less contrast. If the window width becomes more narrow, the result is an image that displays more contrast. Similar to the window level, it is suggested that the radiographer does not adjust the window width because the radiologist's monitor is of higher definition, so it is suggested to allow him or her to make these adjustments if necessary.

Electronic Cropping or Masking

Digital radiology systems offer end users a multitude of postprocessing functions. One such action is the electronic cropping or masking function, which is synonymous with electronic collimation. Collimation performed before the actual exposure has been taken is an essential component of complying with the ALARA principle. Proper collimation helps control the amount of scatter radiation, which will affect the quality of the image. Digital X-ray receptors are extremely sensitive to scatter as it exits the patient, which can affect the contrast of the X-ray that is produced. When electronic masking is used, the physician that is reading the X-ray may not correctly diagnose a patient because the original field of view has been altered and the anatomy may be obscured by these shutters. This concern may prevent departments from using the electronic masking function because it is a definite legal consideration. If it is used because it provides better image quality, department policy may require that the radiographer also submit the original image before the masking was applied.

Stitching

Certain conventional radiography exams required long (36-inch) cassettes in order to display the entire spine or lower extremity so that they could be visualized on one film. The cassettes were heavy, cumbersome, rarely used in some departments so the film expired, and could be difficult to feed into the darkroom processor. Image stitching is a postprocessing function of digital radiology systems that allows the radiographer to "stitch" several images together after taken separately when the anatomical structure is too long to fit in one image. Postprocessing enables the anatomy to appear as if one X-ray was taken. In digital imaging, this can also apply when the physician wants to see the entire spine or when the leg is to be demonstrated from the hip joint all the down to the foot.

Display Monitors

Viewing Conditions

Radiographers should be familiar with the relationship between viewing conditions and image quality when viewing digital images on various display monitors. Not every monitor is created equal, but the image quality also depends on the viewing conditions in the exam and/or reading rooms. The light in the viewing room should be on a dimmer switch so that the person reviewing the images is not required to do so under direct light. Ambient lighting should be dimmed to achieve an optimal reading environment. The display monitor should be adjusted to that it is perpendicular to the operator's eyes so that contrast is not lost. The monitor should be close enough to the user, or in some exam rooms if this is not possible larger monitors should be installed. The monitors should be kept clean, and all users must follow the manufacturer's instructions when cleaning them.

Imaging Informatics

Digital Imaging and Communications in Medicine (DICOM)

Digital Imaging and Communications in Medicine (DICOM) can be thought of as the link between the digital radiography system and Picture Archiving and Communications System (PACS) (or any medical device and the network that it is stored on), and it facilitates the interaction between the two. DICOM integrates the networks, printing devices, workstation, and PACS that were purchased (even when purchased from multiple vendors). DICOM images are very large images, and unlike JPEG images, they cannot just be loaded onto a computer. Windows does not recognize the data from DICOM, and users cannot just double-click to load the image. Instead, a DICOM browser is necessary so the images can be viewed on various computers, workstations, or even CDs. DICOM protocols will enable the digital X-ray system to send the images to the PACS network for archiving purposes.

PACS

The Picture Archiving and Communications System (PACS), allows facilities that use digital imaging to share and archive images electronically so they can be viewed on a network. Physicians and other medical personnel can also access diagnostic imaging reports because they can be stored on the PACS system. PACS has been used to replace film for facilities that have converted from conventional radiography. This not only saves storage space for film and chemicals, but it also allows more than one user to visualize studies at the same time as well as grant instantaneous access to the archived images. Darkrooms are no longer necessary in radiology departments, so these rooms may be converted to other usable space. PACS enables the radiologists and other physicians instant access to prior imaging studies for comparison. The 3D reconstructions are also offered with the reading stations of PACS systems, which is useful for radiologists and surgeons alike.

RIS (Modality Work List)

The radiology information system (RIS) is a specific type of electronic health record (EHR) system that a radiology department uses in order to schedule, track, and manage patients as well as send reports to providers and bill patients. An RIS is an important component of the EHR that helps improve efficiency because the departmental modality work list is linked to it and it eliminates the use of paper forms in the department. For facilities that still use paper forms for some things, they can be scanned in and added to the RIS and attached to the patient's file. Because the RIS communicates with the EHR, fewer errors are made when scheduling or entering patient information so it increases workflow efficiency. The RIS also prevents staff that is not authorized from obtaining patient information. The imaging department can also track supplies via the RIS so that they can be replenished more readily; this can prevent having too many supplies on hand, which saves money.

Electronic Medical Record (EMR)

In a hospital or outpatient clinic, medical personnel use computers or hand-held devices to input patient data instead of writing information in the patient's paper chart. In fact, the patient probably doesn't even have a paper chart because the electronic medical record (EMR) is the digital rendition of the paper charts that were once used. The EMR system can notify a patient for their annual or follow-up appointment and track certain vitals (such as a patient's pulse, blood pressure, or weight). An EMR system can be used for comparisons when following up on a patient, for example, if a patient was diagnosed with hypertension two months ago and put on medication to control it.

The EMR will enable providers to track previous values to determine if the treatment is effective. Also, patient data can be shared among networks to provide integrated care for the patient because all providers have access to patient data such as his or her history, medications, laboratory test results, imaging reports, and allergies.

Quality Control of Imaging Equipment and Accessories

Beam Restriction

Light Field to Radiation Field Alignment

The quality control (QC) program of a radiography department requires various tests that can uncover any variants from the normal operations of the X-ray equipment. QC is an important function that should be performed on a routine basis, and it is required by The Joint Commission. All radiology personnel should make a concerted effort to observe and report defects in order to correct the problem as quickly as possible so that radiographic quality or patient care does not suffer. One such test is the collimator/light field to radiation field alignment. Collimation should be performed on exams whenever possible, but if the light and radiation fields are not aligned, it would be difficult to collimate because the radiographer runs the risk of excluding important anatomy and having to repeat the exposure. This should demonstrate accuracy within 2% of the SID. The light should not be seen beyond the borders of the image receptor. Common causes include careless movement of the X-ray tube or running into it with equipment such as a patient stretcher or a crash cart. This QC test should be performed every 6 months.

Central Ray Alignment

The central ray alignment should be tested every year or when X-ray operators notice a discrepancy in where the beam should be directed versus where the actual beam enters the patient, for example, when a CR system is being used and a cassette is placed in the Bucky assembly but the crosshairs from the light field do not match the lines on the upright Bucky assembly. In this case, the radiographer would want to make sure that the tube is in the correct detent position. Modern equipment will prevent exposure if the tube is not in detent. In cases in which the central ray does not align correctly, the radiographer should not attempt the exposure by trying to guess how to rectify the situation. The patient should be moved to a different exam room, and the engineers should be called immediately. The problem may be due to the location of the tube within the tube housing. If it is not projecting the beam in a perpendicular fashion, it will create images that display distortion of the anatomical structures. In order to pass this QC test, the beam should be within 1% of perpendicular.

Procedures

Head, Spine, and Pelvis Procedures

HEAD

SKULL

The posterioranterior (PA) axial projection of the skull is commonly referred to as the Caldwell method. The radiographer should instruct the patient to rest his or her nose and forehead on the upright image receptor (otherwise known as the upright or vertical Bucky assembly) or the table if doing this prone. The orbitomeatal line (OML) should be adjusted so that it is perpendicular to the image receptor, and the midsagittal plane should be centered to the middle of the Bucky assembly so that no rotation is present. The path of the central ray should be from the back of the skull through the nasion. A 15-degree caudal angulation will demonstrate the petrous ridges in the lower third of the orbits. If no angulation is performed, the petrous ridges will fill the entire portion of the orbits for the PA projection. The patient is positioned the same way for both projections.

The occipital bone forms the posterior and inferior portions of the skull. The foramen magnum is a hole in the occipital bone that enables the spinal cord and brainstem to unite. On both sides of the foramen magnum are the condyles of the occipital bones. These knoblike extensions of the occipital bone form the only articulation of the bony portions of the skull and vertebrae. The joints that are formed in this area are known as the atlanto-occipital joint joints as they meet with C1, which is the first cervical vertebrae. This first vertebra in the cervical (neck) region is also known as the atlas, thus the atlanto-occipital reference. Although fractures of the occipital condyles are fairly uncommon, they can occur and must be correctly diagnosed and may be missed with plain radiographs. MRI and CT have allowed more fractures of this nature to be diagnosed, enabling more efficient management and better patient outcomes.

An AP axial projection of the skull is useful when the posterior section of the cranium is the area of concern; it is also referred to as the Towne method. The areas included on the radiograph are the occipital and posterior portions of the parietal bones, the foramen magnum and surrounding structures, as well as the petrous ridges of the temporal bones. This projection can be performed either upright or on the table. The radiographer should instruct the patient to tuck his or her chin until the OML is perpendicular to the image receptor. It is important to understand that not all patients can flex the neck, so adjustments may be necessary with the central ray. The midsagittal plane should also be perpendicular to the Bucky assembly or the table so that no rotation occurs. The central ray enters the frontal bone and exits the foramen magnum with either a 30-degree (when the OML is perpendicular) or a 37-degree caudal angulation (when the infraorbitomeatal line [IOML] is perpendicular to the image receptor).

The temporal bones contain the external auditory meatus (EAM) and the mastoid processes. The temporal bones of the cranium are located on the right and left sides of the cranium between the occipital and sphenoid bones. There are several components of the temporal bones; the EAM is just one important structure. It is roughly one-half inch long and is created by the tympanic region of the temporal bones. The mastoid processes can be palpated behind the ears on the right and left sides of the cranium, and they provide an attachment site for various muscles. These processes also contain air cells to aid in pressure regulation of the ears. These processes tend to vary in size because some individuals have more air cells than the next person. The mastoid region of the temporal bones joins with the parietal bones superiorly.

Mandible

The mandible is the correct medical term for the lower jaw bone. The mandible anchors the lower teeth, which are necessary for chewing. It is the only movable facial bone, and it joins with the temporal bone to form the temporomandibular joints (TMJs). The condyloid processes are located on the posterior portion of the rami on each side of the mandible to allow the articulation of the mandible and temporal bones at the TMJ. More than one view is necessary to display the various areas of the mandible because of the irregularity of shape and size. In order to best demonstrate the condyloid process and TMJ, the PA axial projection is used. The X-ray tube should be angled 25 degrees cephalad so that the occipital and temporal bones are viewed superior to the structures of interest.

Zygomatic Arch

A tripod fracture is typically seen in male patients after car accidents, sports-related injuries, or any direct blow especially to the lateral portion of the facial bones. Recall that the orbital walls are extremely thin, making them susceptible to fractures, especially in cases of blunt force trauma. In this type of fracture, the zygoma is detached from the normal position. Other factors that help diagnose a tripod fracture include a fracture of the zygomatic arch, an orbital floor fracture that affects the maxillary sinus, and breaks that affect the lateral portion of the orbit as well. The medical term for a tripod fracture is a zygomaticomaxillary complex fracture, but most providers still refer to this type of injury as a tripod fracture.

Temporomandibular Joints (TMJs)

Pain of the temporomandibular joints (TMJs) comprises the majority of facial pain for which patients seek treatment. TMJ disorders may take time to diagnose correctly because pain may be referred to structures such as the teeth, ears, eyes, neck, or even the shoulders. Headaches may be another common symptom of problems with the TMJ. Anxiety may be the cause of TMJ issues (if the individual clenches his or her jaw), grinding their teeth while sleeping (which the person may be unaware they are doing), chewing gum, or the patients may experience issues after dental work. MRI is the preferred modality for TMJ imaging because it evaluates the bony and soft-tissue components. A disadvantage of evaluating the TMJs with X-ray is that this exam only provides information pertaining to the bones such as fractures or other pathology. X-rays should be performed bilaterally for comparison purposes in the open- and closed-mouth positions.

Orbits

A blowout fracture is one that affects any portion of the bony cavity that creates the eye socket. A blowout fracture typically occurs in the inferior portion of the floor of the orbit due to the thin structure of the bone in this region. A blowout fracture is important to correctly diagnose to preserve the patient's vision. A CT scan is the best way to diagnose this type of fracture, but when radiographs are also requested, a parietoacanthial projection (the Waters method) will be performed. The Waters method is performed by having the patient place their chin on the image receptor. The OML should form a 37-degree angle with the image receptor. This flexion will project the petrous pyramids inferiorly out of the orbits to enable the physician better views of the eye socket and maxillary sinus. The central ray should be adjusted to exit the middle of the orbits without any angulation of the tube.

Paranasal Sinuses

The submentovertical (SMV) projection enables physicians to better visualize the ethmoid and sphenoid sinuses. The radiographer should instruct the patient to "flip" his or her head back and rest the top part of it on the Bucky assembly. It may be easier to show the patient what is required for this radiograph and work as quickly as possible because this is not an easy position to hold. The midsagittal plane is perpendicular to the image receptor, and no rotation should be noticed. Recall that for sinus radiographs, it is imperative that the central ray is not angled and the patient must be upright (seated is the preferred position to help the patient hold still) to demonstrate fluid levels, if present. The central ray will be perpendicular to the IOML as long as the patient can extend his or her head back far enough.

Spine and Pelvis

Cervical Spine

Most radiology departments will include an AP axial projection of the cervical spine so the physician can evaluate the third cervical (C3) vertebrae and inferiorly to the second thoracic (T2) vertebra. This can be accomplished with the patient standing or even lying on the table. The radiographer should ask the patient to lift his or her chin just a little to prevent the mandible from obscuring the vertebral body. Make sure that the patient is not rotated and is looking straight ahead. The central ray should be angled 15–20 degrees toward the patient's head (cephalad) in the middle of the neck at the level of C4. The first and second cervical vertebrae are not visualized due to the occipital bone, so some departments may require a separate AP projection in order to display these structures.

Radiographers should be aware that the cervical intervertebral foramina are positioned anteriorly at a 45-degree angle with regard to the midsagittal plane of the body. Due to the location of the intervertebral foramina of the cervical region, if the left intervertebral foramina are to be examined in an AP projection, the patient would be in the right posterior oblique (RPO) position because this will demonstrate the open foramina on the "up" side (the side farthest away from image receptor). The radiographer should position the patient in a 45-degree RPO position with a 15- to 20-degree cephalic angle of the central ray that enters at the level of C4 and centered on the spine. If the right cervical intervertebral foramina are of interest, the patient would be placed in a left posterior oblique (LPO) position because this position places these structures farthest from the image receptor.

When a radiographer performs an AP axial projection of the cervical spine, only C3–T2 will be demonstrated because of the location of the occipital bone. In order to display C1 and C2, an AP projection may be performed and many facilities will use the open-mouth technique. When C2 is of interest, the radiographer can either perform this projection with the patient standing or lying on the table. This level should be centered to the image receptor without any rotation of the head. A perpendicular central ray is used, and once an adjustment of the patient's head is made (positioning an imaginary line from the tip of the incisors to the mastoid processes is perpendicular to the image receptor), the radiographer will instruct the patient to open his or her mouth as wide as possible. This may need to be demonstrated for the patient, or clear instructions should be explained before it is attempted because it is not only a strange projection, but also the position may be hard to hold.

Thoracic Spine

A routine lateral projection of the thoracic spine is supposed to show all 12 thoracic vertebrae; however, a lateral projection may not demonstrate the upper thoracic region well. Many facilities will add a cervicothoracic region lateral projection, which is also referred to as a swimmer's lateral, to demonstrate the upper thoracic region as well as the lower cervical spine. The radiographer can perform this additional image in the same position of the lateral projection of the thoracic spine. The radiographer will ask the patient to raise the arm on the side that is he or she is already lying on while relaxing the other arm as much as possible and then rotating the patient slightly so the humeral heads are not superimposed on the upper thoracic region. The film should be centered at

T2, with the central ray entering at the top of the depressed shoulder. The swimmer's lateral projection should demonstrate C5–T5.

In the thoracic region, the intervertebral foramina are located at right angles (90 degrees) to the midsagittal plane. The best projection to demonstrate the thoracic intervertebral foramina will be a lateral projection, for which the patient is often lying on the radiographic table (although it may be performed with the patient upright). Most radiology facilities prefer a left lateral position, and this is easier for the technologist because the patient will be rolled away from where the radiographer is standing. This position allows better visualization regarding the long axis of the spine when the operator finds it necessary to use sponges to maintain a spine that will be horizontal and parallel to the table. The central ray should be aimed at the level of T7 at the midcoronal plane, and sometimes this will require a slight cephalic angulation so it enters the patient perpendicular to the spine. The angulation is typically performed if the patient cannot be supported enough to obtain a spine that is horizontal, and it is usually only about 10–15 degrees.

The radiographic quality of a lateral thoracic spine X-ray may be enhanced if the radiographer tightly collimates to the thoracic spine. This may be difficult to do with confidence, especially on heavier patients, but by using close collimation, less scatter radiation will be created. The radiographer should also use lead strips to help absorb scatter radiation that is generated by the patient. These strips of lead can be placed on the table posterior to the patient, and if the patient is large enough, they may be placed anterior to the spine as well. If lead is going to be placed directly on the patient, it is best to explain why to the patient before placing the lead strips. Often, more precise technique is required in the inferior portion of the thoracic spine, so make sure to use the anode heel effect properly so that the anode (the + charge) is over the thinner portion. A breathing technique may be preferred by the radiographer to blur lung markings, but this will increase the exposure time.

Lumbar Spine

When performing an AP or PA projection of the lumbar spine, the radiographer must make sure that all of the lumbar vertebrae are visualized as well as the last thoracic vertebra (T12) and the sacrum. Regardless of how this projection is performed, the radiographer must be certain that the patient is not rotated, and this can be evaluated because the sacroiliac (SI) joints should be the same distance from the spine on both sides. This projection will demonstrate not only the bodies of the lumbar vertebrae, but also the spinous and transverse processes, the disk spaces, the laminae, and the pedicles. The radiographer must be certain to collimate to the psoas muscle because the structures lateral to the spine should not be irradiated. The intervertebral disk spaces should be open, and the exposure technique should penetrate all of the aforementioned structures properly without displaying any artifacts on the image.

A radiographer can accomplish a lateral projection of the lumbar spine by asking the patient to roll onto his or her left side because this is typically the position preferred by the physician that is reading the exam. A left lateral position is also the easiest for the X-ray operator because it is easier to determine if the spine is horizontal. The central ray should enter the patient perpendicular to the midcoronal plane at the level of the iliac crest (L4), which can easily be palpated. If angulation of the central ray is required, it typically is a 5- to 8-degree caudal angle. The evaluation criteria include the visualization of the vertebral bodies of T12, L1–L5 as well as the part of the sacrum. The vertebral bodies should be in the middle of the film, especially if the radiographer is using AEC. The disk spaces should appear open, the spinous processes can be seen, and a profile view of the first four intervertebral foramina should be seen. Close collimation should be performed to reduce the amount of scatter radiation from the patient.

A lateral projection of the L5–S1 region is typically part of a routine lumbar spine exam. This can be taken immediately after the lateral projection of the lumbar spine because the patient will be in the same position, but some departments will require the patient to straighten his or her hips during this "spot film." The central ray should be parallel with the interiliac line, which may require a caudal angulation of 5–8 degrees depending on the size of the patient's pelvis. The central ray should enter the patient about 1.5 inches inferior to the iliac crest and about 2 inches posterior to the anterior superior iliac spine (ASIS), which should correlate with the lumbosacral joint to place it in the center of the image. This joint space should appear open on the image, and the radiographer should collimate tightly in order to prevent the image from being degraded from scatter radiation.

A lumbar spine exam will typically include two AP oblique projections in order to demonstrate the zygapophyseal joints on the side that is closest to the image receptor. These oblique projections can be performed after the AP projection so that the patient doesn't have to be rolled on the table as much. In fact, the RPO position should be performed before the LPO position so the patient can easily transition from the LPO to the left lateral. It is helpful to use a 45-degree sponge to help the patient hold this position. Make sure that the spine is straight and it is in the center of the image, and adjust the degree of obliquity while having the patient position his or her arms away from the light field. The images that are obtained during an oblique projection are often referred to as "Scottie dogs," and they can help evaluate if the correct positioning has been achieved because the pedicle, lamina, and the superior and inferior articular processes are well visualized.

Radiographers should realize that when performing AP oblique projections of the lumbar spine, the RPO and LPO positions will be used. AP projections will demonstrate the zygapophyseal joints on the down side or the side closest to the image receptor. In this example, if the patient is in the RPO position, the patient is rolled 45 degrees toward his or her right side. The side that is closest to the image receptor is the right side; therefore, the right zygapophyseal joints are demonstrated. The radiographer should always use the correct lead marker and mark the side that is down. Conversely, when the patient is in the LPO position, the left zygapophyseal joints are demonstrated. Both oblique projections should be included in every complete lumbar spine series in order to see the zygapophyseal joints on both sides.

Typically, a lumbar spine series will be performed starting with the patient supine on the radiographic table, which is an AP projection, but this can be performed PA as well. The oblique projections will be generated in the same fashion as the first image taken whether it is AP or PA. PA oblique projections can be performed with the patient in the right anterior oblique (RAO) and left anterior oblique (LAO) positions. The body is still placed in a 45-degree oblique position, and when done on the table, it is still useful to use a 45-degree sponge to help hold this position. The radiographer can still use the Scottie dogs to evaluate the degree of obliquity, but in this example, if the patient is in the RAO position, the left zygapophyseal joints are demonstrated because when done in the PA oblique projection, it will be the side farther from the image receptor. This is different than an AP oblique projection, which will demonstrate the side closest to the image receptor.

A useful procedure when evaluating an oblique projection of the lumbar spine is to look at the Scottie dog. The pedicle is the eye of the Scottie dog, and if it is found too far anteriorly, the patient will need to be repositioned at a steeper oblique angle. If the pedicle is too far back, the patient was rolled too much, so less of an oblique angle will be required on the repeat exposure. The ear of the dog is the superior articular process, and the leg is the inferior articular process. The dog's body is represented by the lamina, and the transverse process is the nose. Typically, if the patient is rolled 45 degrees into the RPO and LPO positions, these joints will be well demonstrated. Please note that the zygapophyseal joints demonstrated in the lumbar region for the AP projection are closest to the image receptor, whereas in the thoracic region, it is the side that is furthest from the image receptor.

Lateral flexion and extension projections of the lumbar spine may be additional images that are requested by physicians that are concerned about the amount of movement that a patient has if a herniated disk is suspected or has already been diagnosed. The physician may also want to determine the amount of mobility of the spine in postoperative cases of a spinal fusion. These radiographs may be performed with the patient upright or lying on the radiographic table, but he or she will be in a left lateral position. The radiographer should place the patient in a left lateral position and then ask him or her to curl into a fetal position while bending forward as much as possible (flexion). The second image will demonstrate extension, and the radiographer should again start in a left lateral position and instruct the patient to lean back as far as possible during the exposure. These images should be clearly marked flexion and extension so there isn't any confusion in the movement that was attempted by the patient.

If a radiographer notices that the Scottie dog appears to be wearing a collar on an oblique projection, then spondylolysis may be present in this individual. Spondylolysis is a stress fracture of the posterior structure of the vertebra known as the pars interarticularis. The pars is a structure that joins the facet joints of the superior and inferior regions of the vertebra. These stress fractures are often seen in the L5 vertebra, but they may also occur in L4. This defect may affect individuals of any age, but it is often diagnosed in younger athletes that partake in activities that subject them to repetitive stress of the spine, such as football players and gymnasts. If this injury allows the vertebra to slip anteriorly when compared to the level below it, it results in spondylolisthesis.

Sacrum and Coccyx

The sacrum may be imaged with the patient lying on the table in either the supine or prone position, depending on which one is the most comfortable. The AP axial projection is preferred because it decreases the OID, although the amount of detail lost when performing this image prone is not considerable. During the AP axial projection of the sacrum, the patient will be supine on the radiographic table. The radiographer should ensure that there is no rotation of the hips, make sure the spine is straight, and check that the shoulders are positioned in the same plane. The central ray should enter the patient 2 inches superior to the symphysis pubis at the midsagittal plane with a 15-degree cephalic angle. If this view is attempted while the patient is prone, the tube should be angled 15 degrees caudally entering the midline of the sacrum.

If an exam of the coccyx (tailbone) is ordered, two projections will be performed. Typically, AP axial and lateral projections are preferred, but a PA axial projection may be done instead, especially if the patient is experiencing an extreme amount of tenderness that may prevent being flat on his or her back. The X-ray tube should be angled 10 degrees caudally entering the patient 2 inches superior to the symphysis at the midsagittal plane. If it is more comfortable for the patient to lie on his or her stomach, then the central ray should be angled 10 degrees cephalic entering the coccyx. A left lateral position is typically used to position the patient, and the central ray is perpendicular to the coccyx, which is roughly 5 inches posterior to the midcoronal plane. The radiographer may find it helpful to instruct the patient to point to his or her coccyx so it is easier to tell if the beam is centered correctly without having to palpate this structure.

Sacroiliac (SI) Joints

AP oblique projections of the sacroiliac (SI) joints will be performed bilaterally with the patient lying on the table on his or her back. From the supine position, the radiographer should instruct the patient to roll about 25 to 30 degrees to open up the SI joint so there isn't a lot of overlap from the bones of the sacrum and ilium. The correct obliquity can be accomplished with a radiolucent sponge to help hold this position. The X-ray beam should be perpendicular, and the central ray should be centered 1 inch medial to the ASIS on the side that is elevated. Therefore, in the AP oblique projections, the RPO position will demonstrate the left SI joint and the LPO position will demonstrate the right SI joint. If PA oblique projections are performed, the SI joint closest to the image receptor will be evaluated.

Pelvis and Hip

When performing an AP projection of the pelvis or hip, the patient will be in the supine position on the radiographic table. When patients lie on the table with the legs extended, they may be in a neutral or even external rotation. However, in order to obtain a true AP projection of the pelvis or hip, the radiographer must instruct the patient to point his or her toes toward each other (which will rotate the entire lower leg) about 15 degrees medially. This positioning of the feet is done to place the long axis of the femoral necks parallel with the image receptor, and it corrects the anteversion that will be present if the patient does not invert the toes. Most people can hold this position, but sometimes radiographers will have to use sandbags or a strap to hold the feet in this position. This step should be skipped in cases of suspected fractures.

When performing an AP projection of the pelvis, the goal is to demonstrate the entire pelvis as well as the proximal segments of both femurs. In order to display all of these structures, the radiographer will instruct the patient to lie flat on the radiographic table with the legs extended. There shouldn't be any rotation of the body, and the patient's body should be in a straight line. The patient should invert the toes 15 degrees to place the femoral necks parallel to the image receptor. The central ray should be perpendicular and should enter the patient 2 inches superior to the symphysis pubis at the midsagittal plane. It is not suggested to palpate the symphysis pubis, but another way to determine if the central ray is in the correct horizontal location is to direct it to enter 2 inches superior to the greater trochanter (which can be palpated on the lateral surface of the leg). If a patient has had prior surgery of the hip, the entire prosthesis must be demonstrated even if an additional image is necessary.

A bilateral frog-leg X-ray of the hip or pelvis is also known as the modified Cleaves method; it should not be attempted in the case of a suspected fracture. The patient will be instructed to lie supine on the table with the legs extended. No rotation of the hips or body should be noted. Then, the radiographer should ask the patient to bend the knees up as much as possible until everything is set up. Direct the central ray perpendicular about 1 inch superior to the symphysis pubis at the midsagittal plane. At this point, the technologist should ask the patient to relax the legs away from each other until they are at a 40-degree angle. Offer the patient sponges for support if necessary, and make sure that the abduction is similar on both sides, which will position the femoral necks parallel to the image receptor.

When a unilateral hip X-ray has been ordered, the radiographer will position the patient much like an AP projection of the pelvis, but he or she will direct the central ray on the side of the affected hip. With the patient lying flat on his or her back and the legs extended, the radiographer must make sure that no rotation of the pelvis has occurred. The radiographer must make sure to ask the patient to point the toes toward each other (15 degrees medially) to correct the anteversion of the femoral neck. This action will position the long axis of this anatomical structure parallel with the image receptor. The radiographer should locate the ASIS and center the patient 2 inches medial to this landmark at a level that is above the greater trochanter. This centering should include the hip joint, greater trochanter in profile, and the proximal femur. If the patient has had surgery on his or her hip, the radiographer must include the entire prosthesis.

Often, radiographers will find it necessary to perform a cross-table lateral hip X-ray. This is done in cases of a suspected fracture or dislocation because a frog-leg lateral should not be performed. The patient will be supine without rotation of the pelvis. The grid or image receptor will be positioned against the affected hip; it is held in place by a cassette holder, held by the patient, or it can even be held by sandbags. The radiographer will ask the patient to bend the unaffected knee and lift it as high as possible so that there isn't any soft-tissue artifact on the image. This may be difficult for some patients, so a support may be necessary to accomplish this. The X-ray tube is on the unaffected side aimed perpendicular to the femoral neck, and it is low enough to enter the midpoint of the patient's inner thigh. Once the central ray is positioned, the grid may need to be adjusted to be perpendicular to the X-ray beam. In nontrauma patients, the affected foot should be internally rotated 15 degrees medially.

The Clements-Nakayama modification of the hip is used when a physician suspects bilateral hip fractures on a patient, if a radiographer is unable to perform a cross-table lateral hip when a patient cannot lift the unaffected leg, or when a patient has had surgery on both hips. This is performed with the patient supine on the table with the legs extended. However, during this method, the radiographer should not instruct the patient to internally rotate the feet. The central ray will be angled 15 degrees so it is directed down toward the table and the hip joint, and it should be perpendicular to the grid (which will also need to be tilted to do this). If the patient has had prior surgery on his or her hip, the entire prosthesis must be included on the image. Soft-tissue artifacts from the other leg should not interfere with the image.

The Judet method consists of taking two radiographs of the acetabulum in order to diagnose a fracture. This method is not typically performed separately; rather, it is used when additional views of the acetabulum are necessary or to follow up a prior acetabular fracture. This technique can be accomplished by having the patient lie supine on the table and then taking the images in the RPO and LPO positions. The patient should be rolled 45 degrees so the affected side is elevated for the internal oblique position and 45 degrees with the affected side closest to the table for the external oblique. A 45-degree sponge may be used in order to help the patient hold this position. The central ray is perpendicular to the affected acetabulum. The acetabulum should be centered in the middle of the image, and proper exposure technique should be used to penetrate the acetabulum.

Thorax and Abdomen Procedures

Thorax

Chest

The mediastinum refers to the area within the thoracic cavity located between the lungs. The mediastinum is found posterior to the sternum and anterior to the vertebral column, and it contains important structures such as the heart, trachea, esophagus, thymus gland, and a number of lymph nodes and nerves. A radiologist will mention in any number of exams that evaluate the thoracic cavity when a mediastinal mass is present. Masses located in the mediastinum can be dangerous because they can compress important structures such as the trachea or spinal cord that are located in this region of the body. The mediastinum is divided into various portions including the superior, anterior, middle, and posterior divisions. It is important to note that the lungs are not included in the mediastinum, but they are located in the thorax or thoracic cavity.

Recall that SID refers to the source to image distance. In radiography, the source is the X-ray tube and the image receptor represents the film, grid, or detector used to create an image. When performing a chest X-ray, the radiographer should have the patient upright whenever possible to enable a better inspiration and prevent an excess amount of blood within the pulmonary circulatory system. It is easier to obtain an SID of 72 inches if the patient is upright versus lying flat on his or her back. A 72-inch SID is considered to be a longer SID that can be reached in radiography suites, emergency departments, or in patient rooms. This distance is used in order to reduce the amount of magnification of the patient's heart, which increases the image detail. When a shorter SID is used, the amount of magnification is increased, which will decrease the amount of resolution of the image. An SID that is a longer distance will also serve to improve the visibility of the lung markings.

When performing a chest X-ray, the radiographer should perform the exposure on the second inspiration. This method will allow the patient to fully expand their lungs, and in cases in which either the patient is hard of hearing or didn't understand the breathing instructions, this will hopefully prevent the necessity of repeat exposures. When the radiographer is evaluating if the patient's inspiration was sufficient on the image, the ribs within the lung field should be counted. There should be at least 10 posterior ribs seen within the lung field superior to the diaphragm. If an inspiration/expiration exam is ordered, the radiographer should see the diaphragm positioned more superiorly resulting in fewer ribs (at least one less) being visible within the lung field during expiration. Of course, the radiographer should keep the ALARA principle in mind because some patients are unable to take in a deep breath due to various pathological conditions.

Pulmonary aspiration occurs when materials such as food, water, saliva, or vomit are inhaled into the lungs. When an individual is eating, these materials are meant to enter the esophagus, which is referred to as the "food tube" and is part of the digestive system that connects the pharynx (throat) and stomach. When aspiration occurs, and a chest X-ray is performed, the physician should evaluate the right main stem bronchus first because it is larger than the left main stem bronchus. The right main stem bronchus is typically positioned more vertically than the left side so objects tend to enter here more often. The left side is not only smaller, but it also tends to be tilted at an angle away from the trachea or windpipe, which makes it a less likely location for foreign bodies to enter. Aspiration can be dangerous because individuals become more susceptible to aspiration pneumonia if the contents that were inhaled contain bacteria.

It is suggested when performing a PA and lateral projection of the chest to direct the central ray at the level of T7 (the seventh thoracic vertebra). When the horizontal plane is centered at T7, it is about halfway between the apices and costophrenic angles of the lungs. The radiographer must make sure that the patient does not raise the shoulders during a deep inspiration because the apices may not be included on the image. For the PA projection, the X-ray operator should make sure that the centering point aligns with the midsagittal plane so that the lateral portions of both lungs are included. The operator should make sure that the midcoronal plane is positioned about 2 inches posterior to the midline of the film. This typically enables the physician to see the anterior and posterior portions of the lungs. The SID should be 72 inches whenever possible to reduce the magnification of the heart.

Emphysema is a chronic disease of the lungs caused by stretching of the air sacs, which are the functional tissue within the lungs. These air sacs are called alveoli, and if these structures are damaged, the patient typically experiences fatigue, shortness of breath, or coughing because there isn't sufficient gas exchange taking place. This inefficiency of gas exchange often creates lungs that are overinflated, and this can be demonstrated on a chest X-ray. The patient will often present with a barrel chest. When this is visualized, the X-ray operator may not be able to position the patient as recommended for the lateral projection because the chest may be too large from anterior to posterior. The lungs may appear darker, whereas the bases of the lungs may take on a flatter shape instead of presenting as a dome-like structure.

A lateral decubitus chest X-ray is performed to exhibit air or fluid levels. If air is suspected, the radiographer should place the patient on his or her side with the affected side up. When the pleural space contains a tiny amount of fluid, a lateral decubitus chest X-ray will help the physician diagnose this more readily. The radiographer should be sure that the affected side is down so that mediastinal structures do not inhibit visualization of any fluid. The patient should be elevated on a decubitus pad that raises the chest about 5 inches. It is important that the radiographer delay the exposure for about 5 minutes while allowing the patient to lie in the lateral position to enable any air or fluid levels to settle. The central ray must be horizontal in order to demonstrate any air or fluid levels, and it should be centered at T7.

Radiographers should attempt to perform all chest X-rays with the patient upright whenever possible. Not only is it easier to take in a deep inspiration when upright, but there is also a better demonstration of air or fluid levels if they are present. The patient may not always be able to stand on his or her own for a chest X-ray, but if the operator has them sitting upright in a chair or their bed, it offers greater diagnostic value than having the patient lie flat on the back. Of course, it is not always possible to have the patient upright, but there are other protocols that can be followed if air or fluid levels are suspected. For example, have the patient lie in a decubitus position, and be sure to allow him or her to lie on the side for at least five minutes. If the patient is not able to roll onto his or her side safely, a lateral projection (ventral or dorsal decubitus position) can be performed, but, again, be sure to allow the patient to stay in that position for 5 minutes so that air may rise and to allow fluid to settle.

Ribs

When a patient has injured ribs, it is important to discern the level of the injury as well as if the injury is located anteriorly or posteriorly. The level is categorized as upper ribs if the injury is above the diaphragm or lower ribs if the injury occurred below the diaphragm. X-rays for injuries above the diaphragm should be performed with the patient standing whenever possible, and they should be performed with the patient lying down for injuries below the diaphragm. When the anterior, lower ribs are of interest, PA projections should be performed in order to place the anterior ribs closest to the image receptor. PA oblique projections are also routinely performed to correctly diagnose any injury or fractures. The affected side will be elevated 45 degrees while using the RAO or LAO position. Some facilities will also incorporate a mandatory chest X-ray (or at the very least a PA projection) to discern any injuries due to rib fractures.

When performing rib X-rays on a patient, the radiographer must determine if the area of concern is located above or below the diaphragm. When ribs above the diaphragm (upper ribs) are affected, the radiographer should take the exposure on a suspended deep inspiration. This will enable the physician to visualize more ribs within the lung fields. When the upper ribs are being X-rayed, the patient should be placed in an upright position so that the diaphragm is at a more inferior position. When the area of concern is located below the diaphragm (lower ribs), the patient should be examined while lying on the table and the exposure should be suspended after a full expiration. This technique will elevate the diaphragm so that the physician can visualize the lower ribs better because the diaphragm moves more superiorly upon expiration. A higher exposure technique may be necessary for lower ribs because the lungs do not cover the lower ribs.

If a patient has experienced trauma to the posterior upper ribs, the radiographer will position the affected area closest to the image receptor. In this case, because the injury is to the upper ribs, the patient will be standing with his or her back against the image receptor while facing the X-ray tube. Because the central ray will enter the anterior portion of the patient and exit the patient in a posterior location, they are all AP projections. When the upper posterior ribs are affected, the radiographer should also include AP oblique projections in which the patient is rotated 45 degrees. The patient will be in the RPO or LPO position, in which the affected side is rotated so that it is closest to the image receptor. The radiographer must also determine if a routine chest X-ray is necessary, which will include the PA and lateral projections. With ribs above the diaphragm and chest X-ray, the exposures will be suspended upon full inspiration.

If a patient has injured the posterior, lower ribs, the radiographer will attempt to perform the exam with the patient lying on the table because the injury is below the diaphragm. The projections that will be performed are the AP and AP oblique projections. These should be performed upon a suspended expiration to allow the diaphragm to move more superiorly enabling the physician to see more ribs. For the AP projection, the central ray should enter the patient at T10 halfway between the spine and lateral portion of the ribs. When the patient is rolled 45 degrees for the AP oblique projections, the central ray is still directed at T10 halfway between the spine and lateral portion of the ribs. Recall that for AP projections, the affected area should be closest to the image receptor.

There are 12 pairs of ribs in the human body, with 24 individual ribs: 24 ($12 \times 2 = 24$). Ribs are divided into various categories such as true, false, and floating ribs. Pairs 1–7 are considered to be true ribs because the anterior portion of the ribs attach directly to the sternum (via the costal cartilage). The false ribs are pairs 8, 9, and 10. These do not attach directly to the sternum because of their more inferior location; rather, they attach to the costal cartilage of the 7th rib. The floating ribs are pairs 11 and 12 (often also considered to be false ribs) which do not attach anteriorly to the sternum. All of the ribs attach posterior to the thoracic vertebrae. Keep in mind that there are 12 pairs of ribs and 12 thoracic vertebrae.

Sternum

When performing a sternum X-ray, the radiographer should position the patient in the RAO position. These images can be done with the patient upright or on the table. When rolling the patient 15–20 degrees, the heart shadow will actually create a good radiographic window to aid in the visualization of the sternum. The radiographer must not use too much rotation because it will be difficult to see the sternum if the spine is superimposed on it. For PA oblique projections, the central ray should be directed to exit the midsternum and about 1 inch lateral to the midsagittal plane on the side that is elevated. In trauma patients that are unable to lie prone on the table, an LPO position should be used while still rolling the patient 15–20 degrees. A breathing technique should be considered to remove pulmonary markings obscuring the sternum. A shorter SID (30–32 inches) can be used during this projection to improve the image quality.

The sternum consists of the manubrium (superiorly), body (the main portion of the sternum), and xiphoid process (inferior tip). When the technologist is attempting a lateral sternum X-ray, the patient should be upright in order to obtain a 72-inch SID to decrease magnification. In contrast, when examining the sternum via the PA oblique projection, it will require a shorter SID in order to obliterate the posterior ribs. The patient should roll the shoulders back so that the sternum can be adjusted perpendicular to the image receptor to be captured in profile. To help the patient hold this position, the X-ray operator may need to instruct the patient to clasp his or her hands behind the back. The central ray should be aimed at the lateral border of the sternum at the midpoint, which is about the level of T7. The sternum should be free of superimposition from the ribs and shoulder joints and should be visible from the manubrium to the xiphoid process.

Abdomen and GI Studies

Abdomen

The quadrants of the abdominopelvic cavity are often referred to in the medical field, so it is imperative that radiographers are familiar with these four quadrants and the structures within. The umbilicus is the site at which this cavity is split into four regions in the vertical and horizontal planes. Physicians will often refer to a quadrant when a patient is experiencing pain. The four quadrants are the right upper quadrant (RUQ), left upper quadrant (LUQ), right lower quadrant (RLQ), and left lower quadrant (LLQ). The cecum is the structure that makes up the proximal portion of the large intestine and is located in the right lower quadrant. This is an important landmark because the appendix projects from the inferior portion of the cecum. Patients that present with appendicitis may experience periumbilical or RLQ pain, fever, chills, vomiting, and diarrhea. The ileocecal valve is also located in the right lower quadrant, and this is where the small and large intestine merge. The ileum comprises the distal portion of the small intestine.

A KUB X-ray is an AP projection of the abdomen that is performed with the patient lying supine on the table. This is performed with a large detector plate, and it includes all abdominopelvic contents from the area just below the diaphragm to the bladder. The diaphragm does not need to be visualized when the patient is supine. This exam uses a perpendicular central ray at the level of the iliac crest in the middle of the patient's body. Breathing instructions for an abdominal X-ray should be performed upon suspended expiration to allow the diaphragm to move superiorly to reveal more of the abdominal contents. KUB is an acronym for kidneys, ureters, and bladder. The kidney shadows should be visible as well as the liver edges and the inferior portion of the bladder. If the entire bladder is not visualized, the radiographer must take another X-ray of the bladder to include all portions.

During fetal development, the kidneys begin in the pelvis and eventually migrate to their more superior posterior position on the right and left sides of the spine. Most individuals have two kidneys, but if the kidneys fuse together during development, this is known as a horseshoe kidney because they form a U-shaped structure. This is a more common occurrence in males, and although there isn't a treatment for this fusion, it is important to diagnose it as early as possible to help manage any symptoms that the child may have. Some people with a horseshoe kidney may not need any special therapy methods or will go through life unaware of having this condition. Clinical providers may recommend that individuals that have been diagnosed with a horseshoe kidney avoid contact sports because these children and adults may be at risk of injury.

An abdominal series may include a KUB, an upright abdomen, and sometimes even a PA chest X-ray. When free air or fluid levels are suspected, an upright abdominal X-ray will be performed on the patient (typically along with a KUB). The central ray must be perpendicular to these air/fluid levels in order to correctly diagnose this when present. In situations that are impossible for the patient to stand or sit upright, a decubitus position can be performed. It is very important that the radiographer allows the patient to stay in the decubitus position for at least 5 minutes to allow any air/fluid levels to settle. Free air is visualized best when the patient is lying with the side of interest up in the air. Fluid will settle with gravity, so the patient should be lying on the side that is suspected to have free fluid. The diaphragm should be included, and the patient should be instructed to suspend breathing after an exhalation.

Esophagus

When performing an esophagram, the radiologist will start with the patient in an upright position, but the majority of the exam will be performed with the patient in the recumbent position. When the patient is recumbent, it enables the contrast to coat the esophagus more thoroughly. This position is especially useful to demonstrate the proximal esophagus because gravity is not propelling the contrast into the stomach as quickly when compared to the upright position. The RAO position is especially helpful during an esophagram because the patient will be rolled 35–40 degrees so that the esophagus is displayed without superimposition from the heart shadow and the spine. If the patient needs to drink more contrast, this position will allow the patient to do so more readily than having the patient lying on his or her back, but if the patient is unable to lie on his or her stomach, an LPO position would also be acceptable.

Upper GI Series, Single or Double Contrast

An upper gastrointestinal (GI) tract series is often performed as a double-contrast exam in which the patient ingests carbon dioxide crystals to better delineate any abnormalities of the mucosal lining of the stomach or to prevent any lesions from being concealed because of the contrast. When the end goal of an image is to see the fundus of the stomach filled with contrast, the patient should be lying on his or her back (supine). When the patient is supine, the contrast will coat the fundus fairly readily while the body and pylorus of the stomach along with the duodenum of the small intestine are filled with air. When the patient is lying flat on his or her back for the AP projection, the stomach moves toward the head of the patient; this projection allows for the evaluation of the retrogastric components of the duodenum and jejunum.

If a lateral projection is performed during an upper GI series, the technologist and physician will be able to visualize the anterior and posterior portions of the stomach. For the right lateral position, the patient is instructed to turn onto his or her right side while lying on the exam table. With the patient in this position, the technologist will also be able to display the duodenal loop, junction of the duodenum, jejunum of the small intestine, and the right retrogastric area. If the left retrogastric space is to be demonstrated, the radiographer should have the patient stand with the left side against the vertical Bucky assembly. The central ray will need to be centered somewhat higher when the patient is lying on the table (around L1/L2) because the stomach will be located more inferiorly when upright (center at L3).

During an upper GI series, the radiologist or radiographer may ask the patient to turn onto his or her stomach so that the RAO position can be reached. Often, this position is obtained after a PA projection because the patient is already prone. This position will allow visualization of barium filling the pylorus and will allow for movement of the contrast into the duodenal bulb because peristalsis is typically more efficient when the patient is in this position. To obtain the correct RAO position, the radiographer should roll the patient 40–70 degrees; typically, patients that have a larger build will require a steeper rotation than those patients that tend to be smaller in size. The central ray should enter the patient at the L1/L2 level between the spine and the side of the patient that is elevated.

Small Bowel Series

The small intestine is found in the GI tract between the stomach and large intestine, and although it is longer than the large intestine, its name stems from the diameter. The diameter of the small intestine is about 1 inch compared to the 3-inch diameter of the large intestine. Most of the body's ability to absorb nutrients takes place in the small intestine. This tubular structure consists of three regions: the duodenum, jejunum, and ileum. The ileum is the last segment of the small intestine that joins with the large intestine (the most proximal segment is called the cecum) at the ileocecal sphincter. During a small bowel series, spot films are typically performed once the barium reaches the ileocecal valve. At this point of the exam, spot films are typically captured under fluoroscopy while the radiologist uses a compression paddle to improve visualization of this area.

Typically, an exam of the small bowel is performed after the patient drinks the contrast. Sometimes a small bowel series may be performed after an upper GI series upon request because the patient is already swallowing the contrast. However, in cases in which a patient is unable to swallow the contrast, but the ordering physician needs to evaluate the small intestine, an enteroclysis may be performed. This exam will require the passage of a tube into the nasal cavity, stomach, and finally the proximal portion of the small intestine. The contrast can then be administered via this tube in order to reach the small intestine. The radiologist will use fluoroscopy and routine radiographs in order to evaluate the small intestine. This particular exam is not comfortable for the patient when the tube is being placed into the small intestine.

Contrast Enema, Single or Double Contrast

During a contrast enema, the position of the body that will exhibit the splenic flexure free if superimposition is the LAO position with the patient holding an oblique position that is roughly 35–45 degrees. Of course, if the patient is in the LAO position, the patient is face down on the table with the left shoulder on the side that is closest to the image receptor. While in this position, the down side will demonstrate the flexure of interest free of superimposition. If the patient is in an AP oblique position, the splenic flexure will appear open if the patient is positioned RPO because the side farthest from the film is better demonstrated. The hepatic flexure is located on the right side of the patient, and if it is to be free of superimposition, the RAO or LPO position would be used.

During a barium enema, the patient will be rolled into various positions in order to demonstrate all aspects of the large intestine. In order to demonstrate the rectosigmoid portion when the patient is in the prone position, the best method would be to angle the central ray 30–40 degrees caudally in order to free up this region of the colon from loops of bowel that tend to superimpose these anatomical structures. The radiographer should direct the X-ray beam at the midsagittal plane at the level of the iliac crests. This image does not have to demonstrate the transverse colon. Some facilities will also use a perpendicular PA projection in which the patient is positioned the same as is the central ray, but no angulation is used. This should include the entire large intestine to include the transverse portion, along with the hepatic and splenic flexures.

The large intestine can be distinguished from the small intestine not only because of the length or diameter, but because of its appearance. Haustra are the result of various fibers that provide tension within the muscular layer of the wall of the large intestine that generates a sac-like structure. One pouch-like structure is referred to as a haustrum, and all of these structures give the large intestine a lumpy appearance. The function of the large intestine is to help reabsorb water and electrolytes that were not extracted in the small intestine. It also helps the individual get rid of any waste products in a process known as defecation. The small intestine takes on a smoother appearance when compared to the large intestine, and it is responsible for the majority of nutrient absorption.

Surgical Cholangiography

Radiographers that work in hospitals will often be required to provide fluoroscopic images in the operating room, known as a surgical or operative cholangiogram or cholangiography. This exam is performed in order to assist the surgeon by using real-time imaging to determine if the bile ducts are patent. Recall that the bile ducts are the tubes that drain bile that is produced in the liver. The gallbladder stores the bile until it enters the duodenum. This exam is commonly performed when a cholecystectomy (surgical removal of the gallbladder) is being performed because of gallstones. Contrast is injected into the common bile duct by the surgeon, in order to assess for stones that may be lodged within the bile ducts especially when the presence of small stones has been diagnosed on ultrasound, in cases of bile duct dilation, or to help determine any masses within the ducts. Often, the table may be raised 15–20 degrees on the patient's left side during imaging to prevent obstruction of the bile ducts from the spine.

ERCP

Endoscopic retrograde cholangiopancreatography (ERCP) is typically performed after an ultrasound of the abdomen (especially the pancreas, liver, gallbladder, and bile ducts). ERCP is often performed in the radiology department because fluoroscopy guidance is used to assist the doctor in placing an endoscope into the ampulla of Vater (also known as the hepatopancreatic duct). Once the correct location is reached, the physician will guide a cannula via the endoscope into this region so that contrast can be injected into the common bile duct. Fluoroscopy will provide the physician with real-time X-ray capabilities to assess for any pathology of the pancreas or bile ducts. Once the contrast is injected, the radiographer may have to assist the patient in rolling in order to prevent superimposition of the pancreatic and common bile ducts.

Urological Studies

Cystography

This example pertains to an AP axial projection, which suggests that the patient is supine on the X-ray table. When an AP axial projection of the urinary bladder is expected during a cystogram, the radiographer should angle the tube 10–15 degrees caudally. The central ray should enter the patient in the midsagittal plane about 2–3 inches superior to the symphysis pubis. This will enable the physician that is reading the exam to see all of the urinary bladder as well as the distal portions of the right and left ureters (the tubes that allow urine to drain from the kidneys into the urinary bladder) and the first portion of the urethra (the tube that eliminates urine from the body). The technologist should only angle the tube 5 degrees if the neck of the bladder and/or proximal region of the urethra are the areas of concern.

Cystourethrography

A voiding cystourethrogram (VCUG) is an exam that requires the catheterization of the patient in order to fill the urinary bladder. This is often performed in children to assess for vesicoureteral (VU) reflux. The normal path of urine flow is from the kidneys into the urinary bladder via the ureters. In patients that experience vesicoureteral reflux, the urine moves in the wrong direction: in the direction of the kidneys. This study is done to examine the function of the urinary system because the physician performing the test will use fluoroscopy to watch as the patient urinates (voids) to determine if reflux is present. Some patients experience recurrent urinary tract infections (UTIs), so this test is helpful to evaluate the anatomy (structure) of the urethra, bladder, and ureters to determine if any abnormalities are present. Retrograde urography, in contrast, is not considered a functional study because the patient is not voiding.

Intravenous Urography

An intravenous pyelogram (IVP) is an exam of the urinary system that physicians may find useful to interrogate its structure (anatomy) and function (physiology). The radiographer should instruct the patient to void before starting the IVP. The reason this step is important is for patient comfort because this exam requires the injection of radiographic contrast, which is filtered through the kidneys and will eventually reach the bladder. If the bladder is full prior to the exam, a bladder that is overdistended could be extremely uncomfortable or even dangerously full (cases of bladder rupture are rare, but they have been reported). If the urinary bladder is full, the contrast may be diluted, and pathology may not be as apparent. A patient may have common symptoms of back pain or hematuria. This test can aid in the diagnosis of kidney stones, masses, and congenital malformations of the urinary system, or it can be used to demonstrate an enlarged prostate in males.

Routine timed images will be taken after the contrast has been injected during an IVP. AP oblique projections are often part of a routine IVP series within 5–10 minutes after contrast injection. The patient is rolled 30 degrees, which positions the kidney on the side that is raised parallel to the image receptor and offers the radiologist a profile view of that kidney. This example is asking specifically how to best demonstrate the left kidney; therefore, it will be the position that elevates the left kidney from the supine position. The radiographer should turn the patient into a 30-degree RPO position in order to elevate the left kidney. The AP oblique position that will best demonstrate the right kidney would be the 30-degree LPO position because it would place the right kidney parallel to the image receptor. All images should be clearly marked with the time interval on the image.

A routine IVP will require a postvoid image to determine the amount of residual contrast in the urinary bladder. This image is performed on male and female patients in order to diagnose any tumors of the bladder. Many facilities will incorporate a postvoid AP projection X-ray performed with the patient standing. The postvoid radiograph is especially helpful in men older than age 40 because an enlarged prostate may be the reason for residual urine that is visualized in the bladder. Other reasons that a postvoid image is routinely taken is to aid the physician in diagnosing cases of bladder prolapse or even to determine if the location of the kidneys changes dramatically in the upright position when compared to the images that are taken in the supine position. This is known as nephroptosis, which is uncommon, but the kidney will drop into the pelvis.

A radiologist may request the radiographer to take an image of the patient during an IVP in the prone position. A PA projection will demonstrate the anterior regions of the kidneys because gravity will allow filling of these structures. Recall that the kidneys are positioned in the retroperitoneum with the superior poles directed in a more posterior position than the inferior poles. The renal pelvis is also positioned more anteriorly, as are the ureters. Therefore, the prone position will direct the flow of contrast into the proximal portion of the ureter, the ureteropelvic junction, as well as the calyces that are in the inferior portion of the kidneys. This position will also provide compression of the abdomen, which may aid in better visualization of the contents in patients that have a lot of bowel gas present.

Retrograde Urography

Retrograde urography (also known as a retrograde pyelogram) is performed using aseptic technique with the patient in the modified lithotomy position. This position is used because catheterization of the patient's ureter(s) is necessary to perform the exam. This is required so that contrast can be introduced into the renal collecting system in patients that are allergic to contrast (because the contrast does not enter the circulatory system), in cases of renal insufficiency, when hematuria (blood in the urine) is present, or if there is an obstruction of the ureters or kidneys. This exam will aid the urologist to diagnose a kidney stone, mass, or stricture of the urinary system. The urologist may also order this exam to evaluate a stent located in the ureter(s). If the patient is able to communicate during this procedure, he or she may complain of back pain when the renal pelvis is filled with contrast. An AP projection is used as a scout image to demonstrate the catheters in the ureter(s).

Extremity Procedures

Upper Extremities

Fingers

An AP projection of the thumb will require the thumb and the image receptor to be parallel to each other. The patient should be seated; while the thumb is centered to the image receptor, have the patient internally rotate the thumb so that the thumbnail is parallel to the image receptor. The patient may need to grab the fingers of the affected hand with the other hand to hold or pull back the fingers so that they are not in the image. When attempting this position, the radiographer may need to show the patient how to perform this maneuver. The entire thumb should be included as well as the trapezium, which is one of the carpal bones. The AP projection is performed with the thumb resting on the image receptor so there is less magnification versus the PA projection in which there is an increased OID.

If a patient has Parkinson's disease, he or she likely experiences tremors, which could create a blurry image during an X-ray. It is important to explain the procedure to all patients, but in cases of involuntary motion, a few more steps may be necessary. The best way to reduce the likelihood of image blur is for the radiographer to reduce the exposure time. If the exposure time is decreased, there will be less of a chance for image blur. The radiographer must be sure that if changing the exposure time, to set the mA accordingly in order to determine the correct mAs so that a repeat image is not necessary. Other possible ways to reduce image blur from tremors are to use positioning devices such as sponges, sandbags, or even tape to help secure the anatomical structure of interest.

Hand

When performing a PA projection of the hand, the radiographer must be sure that the entire hand (including the distal portion of the forearm) including the soft tissues is clearly visible on the monitor (or film). A centering point that enables the physician to see the fingertips to the distal wrist is aiming the central ray perpendicular to the third metacarpophalangeal joint. When positioning the hand on the image receptor, the patient should spread the fingers apart so that all digits can be seen. The radiographer should be sure that there isn't rotation of the hand or fingers and open joints including all of the interphalangeal and metacarpophalangeal joints. The patient should place the palm of the hand flat on the image receptor and make sure that the wrist is flat as well. The X-ray operator should communicate to the patient that any movement will necessitate a repeat radiograph.

When performing a lateral projection of the hand, the radiographer will instruct the patient to bend the elbow 90 degrees and place the wrist on the image receptor so the metacarpals are stacked on top of each other. Some facilities will perform an extension lateral, in which the fingers are extended straight. Other centers will perform a fan lateral, in which the metacarpals are still stacked on top of each other, but instead of extending the fingers, the patient will fan digits 2–5. This prevents any overlapping of the digits. Regardless of which lateral is preferred, the palm will be perpendicular to the image receptor. The central ray will be centered toward the second metacarpophalangeal joint. A PA projection of the hand will place the palm of the hand parallel to the image receptor.

Recall that an oblique position refers to anything that is not parallel or perpendicular to the image receptor. A 45-degree position is halfway between 0 and 90 degrees. Radiographers must perform at least two projections that are 90 degrees from each other. Often, facilities and radiologists will require more than two projections that will include an oblique projection in order to better assess for fractures or pathology. Routine projections of the hand will typically be the PA, PA oblique, and lateral projections. When the hand is adjusted for a PA projection, the palm is flat on the image receptor with the fingers spread slightly apart. In this position, the thumb will automatically be in a 45-degree oblique position. A lateral projection of the hand will typically place the thumb in a PA position.

Wrist

The PA projection of the wrist is routinely performed during an X-ray series of the wrist. The PA projection allows the visualization of the carpal bones in addition to the distal forearm and proximal metacarpals. The radiographer should ask the patient to make a loose fist in order for the wrist to better contact the image receptor. The technologist should also be sure that the wrist is not rotated. If the spaces between the carpal bones are of greater interest, an AP projection can be done instead of a PA projection. The radiographer may have to instruct the patient roll his or her wrist laterally so that no rotation occurs. It is also helpful to elevate the palm and fingers on a sponge to place the wrist in better contact with the image receptor.

The Gaynor-Hart method is useful if the physician suspects carpal tunnel syndrome to better demonstrate any fractures or any irregularity of the soft tissue. Recall that the carpal tunnel is a narrow area of the wrist in which the median nerve and flexor tendons pass through while moving from the forearm to the hand. However, certain conditions create pressure that can build up in this tunnel and compress the median nerve, which can create symptoms such as numbness, tingling, pain, and weakness of the digits. While having the patient hyperextend the wrist, the X-ray beam can be angled 25–30 degrees entering near the base of the third metacarpal. The patient can either use the contralateral hand to pull the fingers back or use a band to perform the same motion. The palmar surface of the wrist bones will be visualized.

The scaphoid bone is one of eight carpal bones and is located on the lateral side of the wrist in the proximal row. The scaphoid bone is broken more often than any other carpal bone. If scaphoid views are ordered, the radiographer should instruct the patient to place his or her palm flat on the image receptor while centering the scaphoid to the center of the image receptor. The technologist should have the patient move his or her hand into ulnar flexion, which is achieved when the fifth digit is turned out toward the ulna. The central ray should be aimed at the scaphoid bone while collimating closely. The central ray can be perpendicular, or it may be angled 15 degrees to the scaphoid. This can also be demonstrated if the image receptor is raised 20 degrees with a perpendicular central ray.

A Colles' fracture commonly occurs when a patient falls with his or her hands extended away from the body in a prone position. These are common fractures that take place when a patient falls down, or they may occur during a skiing or bicycling accident. These types of fractures are often seen in individuals with osteoporosis, especially elderly females. A Colles' fracture is often referred to as a broken bone of the wrist, although it is actually a fracture of the distal radius. Recall that the radius is the bone of the forearm that is located laterally. When a Colles' fracture is diagnosed, it is typically visualized within an inch of the carpal (wrist bones). Often, the portion of the radius that is fractured is the metaphysis, with a dorsal angulation of the bone due to the wrist being in the dorsiflexed position when the fall occurred.

The wrist consists of eight individual bones (unilateral) that are collectively called the carpal bones. Four bones are in the proximal row, and four bones are in the distal row of carpal bones. Surprisingly, the only palpable wrist bone is also the individual bone that is smaller than the rest. This bone is called the pisiform, and it is located in the proximal row of carpal bones on the medial surface. The pisiform is a pea-shaped bone that, unlike the other carpal bones, does not aid in the movement of the wrist. During a routine PA projection, the pisiform is not visualized well because of its superimposition on the triquetral bone. However, a good method to separate these two bones would be to perform an AP oblique with medial rotation. This can be done with a 45-degree rotation of the wrist directing the central ray at the midcarpals, which will place the pisiform in profile.

FOREARM

An AP projection of the forearm is part of a typical radiographic exam in nontrauma patients. During this projection, the radiographer will instruct the patient to supinate his or her hand so that the palm is pointing up. For some patients, true supination of the hand may require them to lean more to the side (laterally). Choose an imaging plate that is long enough to include the elbow and wrist joints, and direct the central ray to the middle of the forearm. Pronation of the hand will generate an oblique rather than an AP projection of the forearm because the distal radius will be superimposed on the ulna. This medial rotation during pronation also generates an oblique elbow position rather than the AP projection that is desired.

A lateral projection of the forearm is performed by asking the patient to bend his or her elbow 90 degrees and positioning the patient so that the shoulder is in the same plane as the elbow. The X-ray operator should make sure that the wrist is in a true lateral position with the thumb stacked on top of the other phalanges. The central ray is centered at the middle of the forearm, and the field of view must include the wrist and elbow joints. Evaluation criteria of a lateral forearm should consist of the superimposition of many structures including the humeral epicondyles (the radiographer may palpate these during positioning to be sure of superimposition). The head of the radius should be superimposed on the coronoid process of the ulna, and distally the ulna and radius should also be superimposed.

ELBOW

A lateral projection of the elbow is accomplished by flexing the elbow 90 degrees while adjusting the wrist and hand in a lateral position. The X-ray beam enters the lateral portion of the elbow while exiting the medial surface at the elbow joint. The radiographer should palpate the humeral epicondyles to make sure that they are perpendicular to the image receptor as asked in this question. This will demonstrate superimposition of the humeral epicondyles on the radiograph. If the question would have been asked about the relationship between the central ray and the epicondyles, the answer would be that they are parallel to each other. The radiographer must be sure to include the proximal forearm as well as the distal portion of the humerus and be sure that the elbow and shoulder are in the same plane.

The olecranon process can be found in the proximal portion of the ulna and is responsible for the pointy part of the elbow joint. The olecranon serves as an attachment point for the triceps tendon, and it articulates with the olecranon fossa of the humerus. Articulation of these two structures will typically prevent the arm from being hyperextended at the elbow joint. Routine X-ray projections of the elbow include the AP, AP oblique(s), and lateral. To answer this question, the lateral projection is the projection that will demonstrate the olecranon process in profile when the elbow is flexed 90 degrees and the humeral epicondyles are superimposed. A lateral projection of the forearm will also display the olecranon process in profile because the elbow, forearm, and wrist are positioned the same way.

There are three fat pads that are associated with the elbow joint. Typically, these fat pads will be positioned within their corresponding fossae on the distal humeral location. Generally, the posterior fat pad is invisible when a lateral projection of the elbow is performed. The largest fat pad is situated over the olecranon fossa, the smallest is in the region of the radial fossa, and the last one is positioned over the coronoid fossa. However, when an X-ray displays a positive fat pad sign, this will be demonstrated during a lateral projection of the elbow as a lucency posterior to the humerus. Sometimes, the only sign of a fracture will be the visualization of the posterior fat pad that is created when a joint effusion is present and displaces the normal location of the fat pad.

HUMERUS

During an AP projection of the humerus, the radiographer will instruct the patient to roll (supinate) the hand while palpating the humeral epicondyles. Then, once the epicondyles are parallel to the image receptor, the patient can stop turning the palm and hold this position. No rotation of the epicondyles should be visualized on the radiograph, which allows the epicondyles to be well demonstrated. The central ray should be directed perpendicular to the midshaft of the humerus, which would make the central ray perpendicular to the epicondyles in the AP projection. In contrast, the lateral projection of the humerus will place the epicondyles perpendicular to the image receptor because of the internal rotation of the arm. In a lateral projection of the humerus, the epicondyles are parallel to the central ray.

Unfortunately, when a patient is seen for a suspected fracture or dislocation of the humerus, he or she will not be able to abduct the arm or turn the hands for the routine AP and lateral projections. In order to obtain a lateral projection of the proximal portion of the humerus, a transthoracic lateral projection may need to be performed. The upright position is preferred to allow correct placement of the shoulder, but sometimes this may need to be performed with the patient supine. Place the affected arm next to the image receptor while instructing the patient to lift the unaffected arm as much as possible. Palpation of the humeral epicondyles will allow the radiographer to rotate the patient enough so that these structures are perpendicular to the image receptor. The X-ray beam should be centered on the surgical neck, and the exposure should be taken on full inspiration.

SHOULDER

Many facilities will use two AP projections of the shoulder during internal and external rotation of the humerus. These projections can quickly be obtained when performed one right after the other without having the patient move after the first exposure. The only change in positioning will be the position of the patient's hand. Many physicians will want to visualize the sternoclavicular (SC) joint of the affected side as well as the tubercles of the humerus. The image receptor can be positioned crosswise, and once the patient is in the correct position, a good place to center the X-ray beam is 1 inch inferior and 1 inch medial to the coracoid process (which is a hook-like process of the scapula that can be palpated inferior to the acromion). The AP projection in external rotation will demonstrate the greater tubercle in profile, whereas internal rotation will show the lesser tubercle in profile.

The projection of the shoulder that will show a profile view of the glenoid cavity is an AP oblique projection, which is often referred to as the Grashey method. Along with a profile view of the glenoid cavity, this projection will also display a joint space that is open between the glenoid cavity and the head of the humerus (also known as the scapulohumeral joint). As with most shoulder projections, this X-ray is often more tolerable for the patient when performed in the upright position. The patient should have his or her back against the Bucky assembly, and he or she should be rotated so the scapula of the affected side is parallel to the image receptor with the head of the humerus touching the Bucky assembly. The X-ray beam should be aimed at the glenoid cavity, which is roughly 2 inches medial and 2 inches distal to the superolateral edge of the patient's shoulder.

A scapular Y projection is used in cases that involve a shoulder dislocation. Some facilities will also incorporate this projection as part of the routine shoulder exam along with the AP projection with internal and external rotation. A scapular Y projection is a PA oblique projection, so the patient will either be in the RAO or LAO position (facing the image receptor). The side being examined should be placed closest to the Bucky assembly; adjust the degree of obliquity until it is nearly 60 degrees with the Bucky assembly. The central ray should enter the patient at the scapulohumeral joint.

When performed correctly, this will display the scapula in a lateral profile with the coracoid located just below or over the clavicle, and the acromion will be found laterally.

A supraspinatus outlet projection (Neer method) view of the shoulder may be requested when a physician suspects shoulder impingement. Although not typically considered a routine view, this tangential view offers better visualization of the acromion process and coracoacromial arch. This is possible because the humeral head will not be superimposed on these structures and the shoulder outlet will be exposed. This will, however, demonstrate superimposition of the lateral border of the scapula on the humerus when positioned correctly. Radiographers will have the patient stand and will position the patient as if performing a scapular Y view, with the only difference being the caudal angle of the tube. The radiographer should place the affected shoulder against the image receptor and rotate the unaffected side away roughly 45–60 degrees so the patient is in right anterior oblique or left anterior oblique position until the scapula is in a lateral position. The tube should be angled 10–15 degrees in a caudal direction and aimed toward the humeral head. A 40-inch source-to-image distance should be used.

Scapula

For most radiology facilities, routine projections of the scapula include the AP and lateral projections. Typically, these exams will be more comfortable in the upright position. During an AP projection, the patient is facing the X-ray tube with his or her back against the Bucky, so this is not the projection that answers this question. If the patient in in the RAO or LAO position, he or she must be facing the Bucky assembly with the injured side centered to the image receptor. The body will be rotated so that the scapular body is perpendicular to the image receptor, and the arm can be placed in various positions depending on which portion of the scapula is to be interrogated. Visualizing the scapula separate from the ribs is important as well as removing the humerus from the area of the scapula of interest.

Clavicle

An AP axial projection of the clavicle will require a cephalic angulation of the central ray directed at the middle of the clavicle. However, there are many variations in the degree of angulation with an AP axial projection because some facilities request that radiographers perform this in a lordotic position whenever possible. In this case, a 15- to 25-degree angulation is preferred. However, if a patient is examined in the supine position, the lordotic position will not be possible; therefore, a 25- to 30-degree angulation is used. Thinner patients will require more angulation of the tube (even as much as 45 degrees) to prevent superimposition of the clavicle on the ribs. This projection will make the clavicle look more horizontal when compared to a routine AP projection. Also, less of the medial end of the clavicle will appear superimposed on the ribs when compared to the AP projection.

An AP axial projection of the clavicle can be performed by having the patient face the tube and take a step away from the Bucky assembly. Next, instruct the patient to bend backward while resting his or her shoulders against the upright Bucky assembly. Radiographers may find it easier to demonstrate this position for the patient before having them attempt this, and they may stand beside the patient when he or she is leaning back. This lordotic position will place the clavicles at right angles (in a cephalic direction) to the image receptor; the central ray should be aimed at the midclavicular area at a 90-degree angle to the coronal plane. When a patient is able to lean against the vertical Bucky assembly, the radiographer will typically reduce the amount of angulation necessary. When a patient is unable to assume the lordotic position, more angulation of the tube will be required.

Whenever possible, the radiographer should attempt to perform PA projections of the clavicle to place this bone closer to the Bucky assembly and reduce the OID. When the OID is as small as possible, the amount of resolution of the radiograph increases. After a traumatic injury to the clavicle, the patient will not want to lie prone on the table, so the PA projection is performed with the patient standing. The central ray should enter the patient's back and exit the middle portion of the clavicle. PA projections should be performed on the clavicle (and other anatomical structures of the body) in order to lower the dose to the patient (especially structures such as the eyes and gonads). When a PA projection is performed, the central ray is not angled, but when a PA axial projection is being done, the X-ray tube is angled caudally 15–25 degrees.

Acromioclavicular (AC) Joints

The acromioclavicular (AC) joints should be imaged bilaterally in order for the radiologist or the reading physician to compare the affected side to the contralateral side. If the patient's shoulders are too broad to fit on one exposure, it will be necessary to perform these exposures on separate image receptors. To help diagnose a dislocation, the patient should be examined while standing or seated because it could be reduced if examined while in a supine position. First, the radiographer should take an exposure without weights. Next, while using weights that are 5 to 8 pounds, the radiographer should have the patient grab the weights by the straps instead of holding them in their hands. If the straps are not used, it may cause the muscles of the shoulder to contract and any minor AC separation may not be recognized. The radiographer should be sure that everything is set up prior to the exposure because this method can be extremely uncomfortable for the patient. The technologist must make sure that the patient is not trying to support the injured side because it is important that the shoulders are in the same plane.

Lower Extremities

Toes

During an AP axial projection of the toes, the interphalangeal joints will appear open when the central ray is angled 15 degrees in the cephalad direction and centered at the second metatarsophalangeal joint. The interphalangeal joint spaces are not typically seen due to the normal curvature of the toes when an AP projection with a perpendicular central ray is used. Another way to accomplish the AP axial projection would be to use a perpendicular central ray, but by using a 15-degree foam wedge that is placed under the toes. This method will also open the interphalangeal joints as well as the spaces between the metatarsophalangeal joints. The phalanges of the toes should be included from the soft tissues surrounding the tips of the toes to the distal metatarsal bones.

Foot

When performing an AP projection of the foot, the radiographer should angle the central ray 10 degrees toward the patient's heel (posteriorly). This is a dorsoplantar projection because the X-ray beam enters the top of the foot, which is the dorsal surface, and it exits the bottom of the foot, which is the plantar surface. The patient should bend the affected side and place the plantar surface of the foot directly on the imaging plate while making sure that the patient's foot is not rotated (in a vertical orientation). The evaluation criteria of the AP axial projection will include the entire foot from the toes to the talus, which is one of the seven tarsal bones of the foot. The second through fourth metatarsals appear equidistant, but the proximal portions of the second through fifth proximal metatarsals tend to overlap.

When performing a medial oblique projection of the foot, the radiographer should instruct the patient to bend the knee of the affected side and place the plantar surface of the foot on the image plate. From this position, instruct the patient to roll the foot and leg internally until the plantar portion of the foot forms a 30-degree angle with the image receptor. This rotation of the foot and leg may be best accomplished by demonstrating this movement for the patient. The X-ray beam should be perpendicular and centered to the base of the third metatarsal after rotation of the foot has been performed. The foot should be shown it its entirety to include the soft tissue surrounding the phalanges to the tarsal bones on the medial and lateral sides of the foot.

A radiologist may request the radiographer to perform the AP oblique that will best demonstrate the side on which the patient is experiencing pain. This will require the technologist to instruct the patient to roll the foot either medial or lateral so that the plantar surface is 30 degrees with the imaging plate. The medial rotation is typically part of a routine foot X-ray exam in which the lateral side of the foot is best demonstrated. This includes the tuberosity of the fifth metatarsal, sinus tarsi, the joint spaces between the calcaneus and cuboid bones, and the joint spaces between the navicular and talus. The lateral rotation of the foot will best demonstrate the medial portion of the foot. When the navicular bone is of interest, this is a better projection as well as the joint spaces between the intermediate and medial cuneiforms.

Physicians may order a weight-bearing series of the foot in order to best demonstrate the functionality of the bones of the foot and ankle as well as to gauge the alignment of these anatomical structures. When compared to a routine non-weight-bearing foot series, more defects of the hindfoot, midfoot, and forefoot are diagnosed when the X-rays are performed when the patient is upright. When performing a weight-bearing series, the radiographer will include an AP axial and lateral projections as requested. It is important to instruct the patient to shift his or her weight onto the affected side so that any measurements are more accurate. Arthritis is also easier to diagnose when the patient is standing because the joint space of the ankle is decreased when present. The AP axial projection also provides physicians with a better view of the arches of the foot.

Calcaneus

When performing a plantodorsal axial projection of the calcaneus (heel bone), the radiographer should have the patient extend his or her leg while placing the heel on the image receptor with the toes in the air. The X-ray operator should center the X-ray beam at the level of the base of the fifth metatarsal in the middle of the foot. A 40-degree cephalic angulation should be used while having the patient dorsiflex the foot using a band, if possible. The calcaneus should be vertical so that the calcaneus is not rotated. The subtalar joint should also be visualized with the proper technique; two exposures may be necessary in order to demonstrate penetration of the subtalar joint as well as the tuberosity of the calcaneal bone.

Ankle

When the distal tibiofibular joint is to be evaluated, the radiographer can perform the AP axial oblique projection with a 45-degree medial rotation of the foot and leg. This method is performed by asking the patient to extend the affected leg and centering the ankle joint to the imaging plate. If possible, the radiographer should ask the patient to dorsiflex the foot while turning the leg and foot medially 45 degrees. Some patients may require a foam sponge to help hold this position. The central ray should be perpendicular, centered between the medial and lateral malleoli. This projection will allow visualization of an open distal tibiofibular joint with minimal obstruction from the talus. In contrast, to demonstrate the ankle mortise, the patient rolls the foot and leg 15–20 degrees medially to open the joint space between the talus and medial and lateral malleoli.

Stress studies of the ankle are only performed by physicians (orthopedic surgeon, radiologist, etc.) when a patient is suspected of having a ruptured ligament. Often, these ankle injuries are due to eversion or inversion trauma. The provider will manually stress the foot by turning it into excessive eversion or inversion positions (instructing the patient to not move his or her leg) during the X-ray exposure, or the preference may be to perform this maneuver under fluoroscopy. If a ligament is ruptured, the X-ray should demonstrate a joint space that is more pronounced on the affected side. The physician may be required to use a local anesthetic in order to adjust the foot to adequately inspect the joint space if the patient is unable to tolerate this procedure.

The palpable bony projections that are found on both sides of the ankle joint are referred to as malleoli. The medial malleolus is the large bony process at the distal portion of the tibia that serves as an attachment point for the deltoid ligament of the ankle joint. The lateral malleolus is located on the distal portion of the fibula and tends to be situated in a more inferior location when compared to the medial malleolus. The anterior talofibular ligament, which is commonly involved when a patient sprains his or her ankle attaches to the lateral malleolus. A bimalleolar fracture is diagnosed when both of the aforementioned malleoli are fractured at the same time. However, a Pott's fracture can include any combination of bone breaks involving the malleoli (lateral, medial, or bimalleolar) as well as an additional injury such as an ankle dislocation or sprain.

Tibia/Fibula

The lower leg consists of two separate bones: the tibia and fibula. The tibia is bigger than the fibula, and it is located in the medial portion of the lower leg. The proximal portion of the tibia joins with the distal portion of the femur. The medial border of the ankle joint is formed by the bony projection of the tibia known as the medial malleolus. Patients often refer to the tibia as the shin bone. The fibula is the lateral bone of the lower leg, which is smaller in diameter than the tibia. The head of the fibula is located proximally, and at the distal end is the lateral malleolus, which forms the lateral portion of the ankle joint.

Knee/Patella

Evaluation criteria for an AP projection of the knee include visualization of the joint between the femur and tibia. Correct technique should enable the bony detail of the femur, tibia, fibula, as well as the soft-tissue borders at the knee. Superimposition of the patella should be demonstrated on the distal portion of the femur. When correct positioning is performed, the X-ray operator should not see any rotation of the femur or lower leg. The AP projection is performed by asking the patient to lie (supine) on the table and straighten his or her legs. Palpate the epicondyles of the femur to determine any rotation of the lower extremity. The central ray should be directed a half inch inferior to the bottom of the patella. Depending on the size of the patient, the central ray may need to be directed 5 degrees cephalad or caudal or it may need to be perpendicular.

If a provider is evaluating a patient's knees for arthritis, a weight-bearing knee series will be ordered. When the patient is standing, this enables better visualization of any joint space narrowing that may not be evident if the series is performed when the patient is lying on the radiographic table. Often, both knees are examined at the same time with one exposure for comparison even if the patient is experiencing pain in one knee. An AP projection can be obtained by dropping the vertical grid and center to the patellar apices with the central ray perpendicular to the image receptor. Make sure that the back of the patient's legs are touching the Bucky assembly with the knees and toes pointed straight ahead. The patient should be instructed to place his or her weight equally on both legs.

The PA axial projection of the knee is also referred to as the Camp-Coventry method. This projection is obtained by asking the patient to lie on his or her stomach on the table with his or her legs straight. Next, the affected knee should be bent roughly 40 degrees and supported on a sponge to help hold this position. The radiographer should make sure that the leg is not rotated, and the knee should be placed on the more superior portion of the imaging plate. The central ray should enter the popliteal fossa on the posterior portion of the patient's knee, and it should be angled to match the degree of flexion of the patient's knee. The image produced with this method will demonstrate the intercondylar fossa free of superimposition from the patella and demonstration of the femoral condyles. This is helpful if a slipped patella is creating a flattening of the lateral condyle, and it will show evidence of loose bodies if present.

When performing a lateral projection of the knee, it is preferred that the patient lie on the radiographic table on the side that is to be imaged. The affected knee should be bent about 20–30 degrees with the femur parallel to the plane of the image receptor. Palpate the femoral epicondyles, and rotate the patient until he or she appears perpendicular to the cassette. The patella should also be perpendicular to the image receptor. It may be helpful to place a foam sponge under the patient's foot to better hold this position. The central ray should be angled 5 degrees cephalic, and it should enter the tissue about 1 inch inferior to the medial epicondyle. During a lateral projection, the medial femoral condyle is magnified because it is a greater distance from the image receptor. This slight angulation of only 5 degrees should help remove any obstruction of the joint space by this structure.

A tangential projection of the patella is often referred to as a sunrise view, and it may be performed as part of a routine knee X-ray series or requested as a special projection. If the radiographer chooses to perform this projection while having the patient sit on the exam table, the patient should be directed to place the foot flat on the table while bending the knee(s) as much as possible. This flexion will adjust the patella so that it is perpendicular to the cassette. The patient will be required to hold the cassette steady as it rests on his or her distal thigh if the X-ray is performed while the patient is seated. The central ray will enter the joint space between the femur and patella with the angulation aimed at the patient's head and upper body. The amount of angulation required will depend on how well the patient is able to bend his or her knee because more flexion equals less angulation. This projection will demonstrate a profile view of the patella and an open joint space between the femur and patella.

Femur

A routine femur radiographic series will include AP and lateral projections of the femur. Often, due to the length of the femur, the radiographer will be required to take separate images of the upper and lower portions of the femur. The X-ray operator must be sure to overlap a segment of the femur according to the protocols of the facility so that the radiologist is confident that the entire femur is included in the images. The lateral projection doesn't display the protuberance of the greater and lesser trochanters because in cases in which a fracture is not suspected, the patient will be rolled on the side that is being investigated. An AP projection of the femur will demonstrate the protuberance of the greater trochanter because it is located at the proximal portion of the body of the femur on the lateral surface. The lesser trochanter is found on the posteromedial surface.

If a patient has had a previous surgery of the femur, the radiographer must be certain to demonstrate the entire orthopedic prosthesis, pins, screws, or plates. This is especially important in trauma-related cases such as a fall or any injury that may have created any movement or dislocation of the orthopedic appliance. The entire prosthesis, pins, screws, or plates should also be evaluated in order to diagnose any infection such as osteomyelitis or any evidence of gas surrounding the appliance. It is important to include any prior studies for the radiologist for comparison purposes. This protocol also applies if an AP projection of the pelvis is ordered and the patient has had a total hip replacement. Depending on the length of the prosthesis, the X-ray operator may need to perform an additional X-ray to include the distal end of the appliance.

Long Bone Measurement

A radiographic exam that is ordered to assess the measurements of long bones is completed because there is a discrepancy in the length of the extremities, and it is therefore performed bilaterally for comparison. Although the upper extremities can be imaged if necessary, it is typically the legs that are interrogated. Pediatric patients are commonly examined for differences in extremity length and are usually reevaluated every year. If surgery is warranted, then long bone measurements will be required more than once a year. When performing long bone measurement exams, it is extremely important that the patient does not move to prevent having to repeat the radiographs. When evaluating the lower extremities, the ruler can be placed between the legs with AP projections taken at the hip, knee, and ankle joints on the same image. If the legs are only about 5–6 inches apart, this will allow the inclusion of both joints.

Other

Bone Age

A bone age radiograph is a quick and painless exam that is performed to determine the skeletal development of a child. One PA radiograph of the left hand and wrist is taken so that the bone age can be determined by evaluating the ossification centers and the amount of calcium present in these anatomical structures. This type of exam is typically done for pediatric patients that appear small in stature for their age, but patients that appear very tall for their age may also be assessed. Bone age radiographs are usually ordered by pediatricians, pediatric orthopedic surgeons, or pediatric endocrinologists to determine if the child's height is due to skeletal or endocrine disorders, the nutritional status of the patient, or even genetic components. Follow-up radiographs can be compared with the initial X-ray, especially in cases in which the child was put on growth hormones to determine their efficiency.

Special Report - Difficult Patients

Every radiology technician will eventually get a difficult patient on their list of responsibilities. These patients can be mentally, physically, and emotionally combative in many different environments. Consequently, care of these patients should be conducted in a manner for personal and self-protection of the technician. Some of the key guidelines are as follows:

- Never allow yourself to be cornered in a room with the patient positioned between you and the door.
- Don't escalate the tension with verbal bantering. Basically, don't argue with the patient or resident.
- Ask permission before performing any normal tasks in a patient's room whenever possible.
- Discuss your concerns with the nursing staff. Consult the floor supervisor if necessary, especially when safety is an issue.
- Get help from other support staff when offering care. Get a witness if you are anticipating abuse of any kind.
- Remove yourself from the situation if you are concerned about your personal safety at all times.
- If attacked, defend yourself with the force necessary for self-protection and attempt to separate from the patient.
- Be aware of the patient's medical and mental history prior to entering the patient's room.
- Don't put yourself in a position to be hurt.
- Get the necessary help for all transfers, bathing and dressing activities from other staff members for difficult patients.
- Respect the resident and patient's personal property.
- Get assistance quickly, via the call bell or vocal projection, if a situation becomes violent or abuse.
- Immediately seek medical treatment if injured.
- Fill out an incident report for proper documentation of the occurrence.
- Protect other patients from abusive behavior.

Special Report – Guidelines for Universal Precautions

Universal precautions are precautions taken to avoid contracting various diseases and preventing the spread of disease to those who have compromised immunity. Some of these diseases include human immunodeficiency virus (HIV), acquired immunodeficiency syndrome (AIDS), and hepatitis B (HBV). Universal precautions are needed since many diseases do not display signs or symptoms in their early stages. Universal precautions mean to treat all body fluids/ substances as if they were contaminated. These body fluids include but are not limited to the following blood, semen, vaginal secretions, breast milk, amniotic fluid, feces, urine, peritoneal fluid, synovial fluid, cerebrospinal fluid, secretions from the nasal and oral cavities, and lacrimal and sweat gland excretions. This means that universal precautions should be used with all patients.

- A shield for the eyes and face must be used if there is a possibility of splashes from blood and body fluids.
- If possibility of blood or body fluids being splashed on clothing, you must wear a plastic apron.
- Gloves must be worn if you could possibly come in contact with blood or body fluids. They are also needed if you are going to touch something that may have come in contact with blood or body fluids.
- Hands must be washed even if you were wearing gloves. Hands must be washed and gloves must be changed between patients. Wash hands with at a dime size amount of soap and warm water for about 30 seconds. Singing "Mary had a little lamb" is approximately 30 seconds.
- Blood and body fluid spills must be cleansed and disinfected using a solution of one part bleach to 10 parts water or your hospital's accepted method.
- Used needles must be separated from clean needles. The sharps' container is made of puncture proof material.
- Take extra care in performing high-risk activities that include puncturing the skin and cutting the skin.
- CPR equipment to be used in a hospital must include resuscitation bags and mouthpieces.

Special precautions must be taken to dispose of biomedical waste. Biomedical waste includes but is not limited to the following: laboratory waste, pathology waste, liquid waste from suction, all sharp object, bladder catheters, chest tubes, IV tubes, and drainage containers. Biomedical waste is removed from a facility by trained biomedical waste disposers.

The health care professional is legally and ethically responsible for adhering to universal precautions. They may prevent you from contracting a fatal disease or from a patient contracting a disease from you that could be deadly.

Special Report - Basic Review of Types of Fractures

A fracture is defined as a break in a bone that may sometimes involve cartilaginous structures. A fracture can be classified according to its cause or the type of break. The following definitions are used to describe breaks.

- Traumatic fracture—break in a bone resulting from injury
- Spontaneous fracture—break in a bone resulting from disease
- Pathologic fracture—another name for a spontaneous fracture
- Compound fracture—occurs when fracture bone is exposed to the outside by an opening in the skin
- Simple fracture—occurs when a break is contained within the skin
- Greenstick fracture—a traumatic break that is incomplete and occurs on the convex surface of the bend in the bone
- Fissured fracture—a traumatic break that involves an incomplete longitudinal break
- Comminuted fracture—a traumatic break that involves a complete fracture that results in several bony fragments
- Transverse fracture—a traumatic break that is complete and occurs at a right angle to the axis of the bone
- Oblique fracture—a traumatic break that occurs at an angle other than a right angel to the axis of the bone.
- Spiral fracture—a traumatic break that occurs by twisting a bone with extreme force

A compound fracture is much more dangerous than a simple break. This is due to the break in skin that can allow microorganisms to infect the injured tissue. When a fracture occurs, blood vessels within the bone and its periosteum are disrupted. The periosteum, covering of fibrous connective tissue on the surface of the bone, may also be damaged or torn.

CPR Guidelines for Professional Rescuers

Topic	Adult	Child	Infant
	Past puberty	1 y/o - puberty	Under 1 y/o
Conscious Choking	abdominal thrusts (or chest thrusts in pregnant/obese)	abdominal thrusts	5 back slaps and 5 chest thrusts in infant
Unconscious Choking	Begin chest compression. Look in the victim's mouth for foreign body before giving breaths.		
Rescue Breaths Normal breath given over 1 second until chest rises.	10-12 breaths per minute (1 breath every 6-8 seconds)	12-20 breaths per minute (1 breath every 3-5 seconds)	20 breaths per minute (1 breath every 3 seconds)
Chest Compressions to Ventilation Ratios (Single Rescuer)	30:2		
Chest Compressions to Ventilation Ratios (Two Rescuer)	30:2	15:2	
Chest Compression rate	At least 100/minute		
Chest Compression Land Marking Method	two hands center of the chest, even with nipples	one hand center of the chest even with nipples	2 or 3 fingers, just below the nipple line at the center of the chest
Chest Compression Depth	At least 2" compression (hands overlapping)	about 2" compression or 1/3 the AP diameter (only heel of one hand)	about 1 ½" compression or 1/3 the AP diameter (2 fingers)
Activate Emergency Response System	As soon as you realize that the victim is unresponsive	After 5 cycles of CPR	After 5 cycles of CPR

Checklist:

- Check the scene
- Check for responsiveness – ask, "Are you OK?"
- Adult - call 911, then administer CPR
- Child/Infant – administer CPR for 5 cycles, then call 911
- Open victim's airway and check for breathing
- Two rescue breaths should be given, 1 second each, and should produce a visible chest rise
- If the air does not go in, reposition and try 2 breaths again
- Check victim's pulse – chest compressions are recommended if an infant or child has a rate less than 60 per minute with signs of poor perfusion
- Continue 30:2 ratio until victim moves, AED is brought to the scene, or professional help arrives

Radiography Practice Test

Want to take this practice test in an online interactive format?
Check out the bonus page, which includes interactive practice questions and much more: **https://www.mometrix.com/bonus948/radiography**

SCAN HERE

1. Which material should be used as the primary shielding around a beta-emitting radionuclide, such as phosphorus-32?

a. Lead, because high-density metals absorb most particle radiation
b. Plexiglas, because beta particles striking it are converted to harmless Bremsstrahlung radiation
c. Lead, because absorbers with larger atomic nuclei block radiation better than absorbers with smaller atomic nuclei
d. Plexiglas, because absorbers with larger atomic nuclei produce more Bremsstrahlung radiation than absorbers with smaller atomic nuclei

2. On average, an individual living in the United States receives approximately how much ionizing radiation from the natural environment per year?

a. None
b. 3 microsieverts (μSv)
c. 3 millisieverts (mSv)
d. 30 millisieverts (mSv)

3. When x-rays strike a human body, which of the following may occur?

a. Cells may be damaged, leading to cell death, or they may repair themselves
b. Cells may be damaged, then repair themselves incorrectly, leading to disease
c. X-rays may pass through the body, or bounce off it, without affecting cells
d. All of the above

4.Factors affecting the dose of ionizing radiation that an individual receives as a result of exposure to a radiation source in the work environment include all of the following EXCEPT?

a. The number of coworkers who work with, or in proximity to, the radiation source
b. The shielding around the radiation source
c. The distance between the individual and the radiation source
d. The amount of time that the individual is exposed to the radiation source

5. A technician receives an exposure to ionizing radiation of approximately 2 μSv per week while sitting 1 meter from a medical x-ray source. If the technician's distance from the x-ray source were moved to 3 meters, the weekly exposure would be:

a. 0.67 μSv
b. 6 μSv
c. 0.5 μSv
d. 0.22 μSv

6. Which of the following pairings of radiation source and dosage of ionizing radiation received during one event is typical?

a. 1 millisievert (mSv) for an adult patient imaged with flat film chest x-rays
b. 40 millisieverts (mSv) for an adult patient imaged with full body computed tomography (CT) scanning
c. 50 microseiverts (μSv) for a patient given dental x-rays
d. 10 microseiverts (μSv) for a passenger flying from New York to San Francisco

7. Which of the following is NOT true regarding radiation monitoring badges?

a. They protect the wearer against most types of ionizing radiation
b. Radiographers must wear them at all times when working in the vicinity of a radiation source
c. They should be placed on the torso, between the waste and the neck
d. When not being worn, they should be kept away from radiation sources

8. Iodine-125 (125I) is a low-energy gamma-emitting isotope that is used in brachytherapy for certain tumors, such as carcinoma of the prostate. Which of the following is MOST accurate regarding the type of hazard that this isotope presents?

a. It is mainly an external exposure hazard because gamma radiation penetrates biological tissue deeply
b. The dangers from external versus internal exposure are approximately equal
c. It is more of a danger when the exposure is internal because it is taken up easily by the thyroid gland
d. It is a hazard only when exposure is internal because of the low energy of its gamma decay

9. X-rays and gamma rays are absorbed effectively by which of the following materials?

a. Lead
b. Barium sulfate
c. Depleted uranium
d. All of the above

10. The linear no-threshold model (LNT) of radiation biological effects is derived from all of the following ideas EXCEPT:

a. Cells have the capability of repairing radiation-induced damage to DNA
b. Any dose of ionizing radiation, even a tiny dose, increases the chance that a cell will undergo malignant change
c. The risk of undesirable biological effects increases as the cumulative radiation exposure of an individual increases
d. The risk of undesirable biological effects, such as malignancy, is proportional to the amount of ionizing radiation to which an individual is exposed

11. Which of the following materials is/are effective in shielding against alpha radiation?

a. Lead aprons
b. A glass window
c. Surgical scrubs
d. All of the above

12. A radiography technician declares to her supervisor that she is pregnant. The radiation dose limit that she permitted to receive over the course of her pregnancy is:

a. 50 microsieverts (μSv)
b. 5 millisieverts (mSv)
c. 50 millisieverts (mSv)
d. 500 millisieverts (mSv)

13. When electrical current is supplied to an x-ray tube:

a. Electrons flow from the anode to the cathode
b. X-ray photons are emitted, moving in a direction opposite that of the electrons
c. Approximately 1 percent of the energy is converted to x-radiation
d. Much of the energy is converted to alpha particles and heat

14. Voltage supplied to an x-ray tube in projection radiography for diagnostic purposes generally is in the range of:

a. 30 to 150 kilovolts (kV)
b. 150 to 500 kV
c. 500 to 1,000 kV
d. 1,000 to 1,250 kV

15. Which of the following statements is accurate regarding tomography?

a. Computed tomography (CT) scanning uses gamma rays
b. Single-photon emission computed tomography (SPECT) uses x-rays
c. Radio waves used in magnetic resonance imaging (MRI) are a form of ionizing radiation
d. Positron emission tomography (PET) makes use of a device that detects gamma rays

16. Foggy or blurry x-ray images can result from all of the following EXCEPT:

a. Leakage of light into dark rooms
b. Improper placement of lead aprons or shields
c. Dirty photographic plates or cassettes
d. Warped photographic plates or cassettes

17. The wavelength (λ) of an x-ray beam can be shortened by:

a. increasing the current
b. decreasing the current
c. decreasing the voltage
d. increasing the voltage

18. The intensity of an x-ray image can be increased by:

a. increasing the mAs
b. decreasing the current while increasing the time that the beam is turned on
c. decreasing the voltage (kV) and/or the time that the beam is on
d. increasing the voltage (kV) and/or the time that the beam is on

19. As part of the routine evaluation of automatic film processing equipment, how often should pH values be tested in developer tanks, fixer tanks, and replenishers?

a. Once per hour
b. Twice per day
c. Once per day
d. Once per week

20. How often must projection x-ray equipment be calibrated?

a. Every day
b. Once per week
c. Once per month
d. Once per year

21. Sensitometric checks to evaluate the quality of film processing in automatic processors require measurements of temperature, fogging, average gradient, and speed. Which of these four properties must be plotted against the other three to create three sets of graphs that can be compared with figures supplied by the manufacturer?

a. Temperature
b. Fogging
c. Average gradient
d. Speed

22. Standard, flat film radiography is performed commonly in the workup for all of the following conditions EXCEPT?

a. A fracture of the triquetrum bone of the wrist
b. Pneumonia
c. A torn anterior cruciate ligament (ACL) in the knee
d. Osteosarcoma in a long bone of an extremity

23. The quality of an x-ray image that a radiographer can obtain can be compromised easily by which of the following conditions?

a. Obesity
b. Diabetes mellitus
c. Atherosclerosis
d. All of the above

24. Media made from radio-opaque material are used frequently with x-rays in the acquisition of images for the purpose of:

a. Protecting the patient against biological effects of radiation
b. Providing positive contrast for the imaging of structures or fluids that normally are not imaged easily
c. Providing negative contrast to enable the imaging of dense structures that may be hidden
d. Making certain anatomic structures temporarily radioactive to enhance their visualization

25. X and gamma radiation differ in that:

a. X-rays are part of the electromagnetic spectrum, whereas gamma radiation consists of particles known as gamma particles
b. X-rays are of lower energy and thus of shorter wavelength as compared with gamma rays
c. Gamma rays are of higher energy, and thus of higher frequency as compared with x-rays
d. X-rays are generated from electrons external to atomic nuclei, whereas gamma rays come from atomic nuclei, or from the annihilation of opposite subatomic particles

26. Which of the following statements is most accurate, regarding the control of the range of wavelengths in an x-ray beam?

a. The minimum wavelength depends on the voltage, whereas the maximum wavelength depends the filtration
b. The minimum wavelength depends on the filtration, whereas the maximum wavelength depends the voltage
c. Both the minimum wavelength and the maximum wavelength depend on the filtration
d. The maximum wavelength depends on the voltage, while the purpose of the filters is to reduce the amount of scattering

27. The quality of an x-ray beam is assessed in terms of which of the following?

a. The attenuation coefficient
b. The half-life
c. The half-value layer
d. The radiographic density

28. Radiographic contrast can be improved by which of the following?

a. Decreasing the voltage supplied to the x-ray tube
b. Decreasing the current supplied to the x-ray tube
c. Decreasing the amount of scattering
d. Decreasing the amount of time that the beam is turned on

29. Bone is more radio-opaque than fat because:

a. Bone has more water than fat has; thus, more photons are absorbed
b. More electrons are available to absorb the energy of x-ray photons
c. Bone has fewer cells and more non-living tissue
d. None of the above

30. Which of the following is MOST accurate, regarding the effects of fat on flat radiography and computed tomography (CT) scanning?

a. Fat adds radiographic contrast to elucidate organs and other structures
b. Fat is more radiolucent than bone, but less radiolucent than soft tissue
c. Since they have very little fat, anorexic patients and others with extremely low fat-to-lean body mass ratios produce images of higher quality, as compared with individuals of mesomorphic (normal) body habitus
d. Obese patients do not present any particular difficulty in terms of image quality because fat is fairly radiolucent

31. An acceptable anteroposterior (AP) or posteroanterior (PA) chest radiograph should show all of the following anatomic features EXCEPT:

a. Medial and lateral lung fields
b. The heart
c. The trachea, covering the upper thoracic vertebrae
d. At least 8 posterior ribs

32. A radiograph that is described as "overpenetrated" is associated with which of the following?

a. Too much current (mAs) supplied to the x-ray tube
b. Bones appearing very lucent
c. Not enough voltage (kVp) supplied to the x-ray tube
d. All of the above

33. A standard PA chest radiograph is taken with the patient:

a. supine, with the x-ray beam aimed at the chest
b. standing, with the x-ray beam aimed at the chest
c. standing, with the x-ray beam aimed at the back
d. prone, with the x-ray beam aimed at the back

34. Which of the following statements is true regarding the PA orientation versus the AP orientation for chest radiography?

a. Silhouettes of both the heart and mediastinum appear larger in the AP view, compared with the PA view
b. Silhouettes of both the heart and mediastinum appear larger in the PA view, compared with the AP view
c. The heart appears larger in AP than PA orientation, while the mediastinum appears larger in PA than AP orientation
d. The heart appears smaller in AP than PA orientation, while the mediastinum appears smaller in PA than AP orientation

35. The rinse medium in a film processor is found to have a residual ammonium thiosulfate level of 31 μgm/in2. What is likely to happen to the film within 1 year?

a. It will appear brown
b. It will appear yellow
c. The film density will appear very low
d. It will appear gray, with a lot of contrast

36. Streaks on a radiographic film following manual processing may be the result of which of the following?

a. Developing solution on the film prior to processing
b. Fixer on the film prior to processing
c. Temperature differences between processing solutions
d. Developing solution on the hangar clips

37. A radiographer processing a film manually places a film in the development tank, then removes if after the timer sounds, indicating that the appropriate amount of time has passed. After rinsing the film, however, she notices that the film is less developed toward the bottom than from the middle to the top. The most likely problem is that:

a. the timer has malfunctioned
b. the lower part of the film was exposed to solution from the fixing tank
c. light leaked into the dark room
d. the solution at the bottom of the development tank is colder than the solution at the top

38. Which of the following is NOT an accurate statement regarding the potential of digital radiography?

a. It can improve the quality of radiographic images, if used correctly
b. It will not reduce the need for repeat radiographs resulting from errors in radiographic technique
c. It can speed up radiographic studies
d. It will reduce the amount of storage space needed

39. Half of an unused film is developed, fixed, washed, and dried, while the other half is fixed, washed, and dried, without first being developed. The densities of the two halves of the film then are compared. The difference between these two densities is known as:

a. development fog
b. exposure fog
c. radiographic mottle
d. radiographic noise

40. Overdevelopment of a radiographic film can be caused by:

a. lower than optimal temperature of the developing solution
b. contamination of the developing solution with fixer
c. incorrectly mixed developer
d. removing the film from the developer too early

41. Grit on a radiographic film can be caused by:

a. developing solution on the film prior to processing
b. fixer on the film prior to processing
c. temperature differences between processing solutions
d. dirty water or dirt in automatic film processing equipment

42. Computed tomography (CT) scanning often makes use of various contrast media that tend to be based on which of the following chemical elements?

a. Barium
b. Bromine
c. Iodine
d. Fluorine

43. Which of the following features of MRI makes it a particularly good choice for imaging the heart, brain, connective tissue, muscles, and neoplasia?

a. Good contrast between various soft tissues
b. The patient is not exposed to ionizing radiation
c. It is safe for patients with cardiac pacemakers and various implants
d. It is relatively simple and cheap, compared with other imaging modalities

44. An image is needed of the occipital bone, foramen magnum, and dorsum sellae. The patient is told to depress her chin, while the central ray (CR) of the x-ray beam is angled 30 degrees toward the patient's feet, passing 2.5 inches above the glabella. This is known as the:

a. Caldwell method
b. Towne method
c. lateral skull position
d. AP skull position

45. For a radiograph of the shoulder seen in internal rotation, the patient should be instructed to:

a. extend the upper extremity, with the forearm supinated
b. extend the upper extremity, with the forearm pronated
c. place the palmar side of the hand against the thigh
d. place the dorsal side of the hand against the thigh

46. To allow for an oblique PA projection of the patella of the knee, a patient is positioned prone, with the affected knee flexed slightly and the hip of the same leg elevated. The central ray (CR) is aimed 30 degrees caudal at the joint space between the femoral condyles and the patella. This is known as the:

a. Judet view
b. Kuchendorf method
c. Johnson method
d. Lilienfeld position

47. Regarding the administration of contrast media, which of the following statements is MOST accurate?

a. A metal needle is preferred to a plastic cannula
b. Drip infusion is preferable to bolus or power injection
c. If a patient feels swelling or pain at the injection site, the injection must be stopped
d. A radiologist must be present whenever a radiographic technician administers contrast medium

48. A pregnant 28-year-old woman, in her 20th gestational week, is sent to x-ray for what appears to be a fracture of one of the carpal bones of the wrist. After noting that she just arrived in the country a few days ago from Europe, the patient expresses concern that exposure to x-rays might harm her fetus. You are a radiographic technician with 10 years of experience. The appropriate response is to:

a. suggest that the patient discuss her concerns with the radiologist
b. call the emergency department physician or the orthopedist who ordered the x-ray and ask if it is really necessary
c. explain that in your 10 years you have performed radiographic procedures on many pregnant women, with no ill effects to their fetuses
d. explain that the dose of ionizing radiation that might reach her fetus is quite small, compared with the exposure that she received during her flight from Europe to the United States

49. You are a radiographic technician at a small community medical center where a simple, flat film radiography is ordered for 10-year-old boy to assess a possible fracture of the right tibia. When the film processing is complete, you remove the film from the automatic processor and it appears acceptable. You also notice an obvious fracture spanning the tibial shaft. Crossing the hallway to deliver the film to the emergency room physician, you run into the boy's mother, who asks, "Is it broken? Will he need a cast?" What is the appropriate response?

a. Explain that you are not a physician and therefore not the one who interprets the radiograph
b. Say that you think it probably is fractured and that the boy probably will need a cast
c. Say that it certainly looks like a fracture, but it is up to the physician to decide on the treatment
d. Pretend not to hear her and walk into the nearest room as quickly as you can

50. Prior to an MRI study, a patient should be told to remove, have removed, or leave aside all of the following EXCEPT:

a. Earrings and other jewelry
b. Body piercings
c. Dental fillings
d. Credit cards

Answer Key and Explanations

1. D: Bremsstrahlung radiation consists of x-rays that are produced when high-velocity electrons interact with shielding materials. Electrons emitted from the nuclei of many radioactive isotopes (radionuclides) are known as beta particles. Beta particles are less harmful to biological tissue than other types of ionizing radiation, while Bremsstrahlung radiation is quite harmful. Nevertheless, high-energy beta emitters such as phosphorus-32 do require some type of shielding. Since the magnitude of Bremsstrahlung radiation produced when beta particles strike an absorber is proportional to the absorber's atomic number, the primary shielding around a beta emitter should consist of small atoms. Thus, polymethyl methacrylate (PMMA), known commonly by the trade names Plexiglas, Lucite, and Perspex, is used around beta emitters. Although lead cannot be used as primary shielding, it is appropriate as secondary protection, placed outside of the PMMA shield.

2. C: Ionizing radiation comes from a variety of natural sources. Galactic cosmic radiation consists of gamma rays, x-rays, neutrons, and heavy particles resulting from explosions of distant stars. Solar particle events send particles from the Sun toward Earth, while the Sun's regular activity sends out x-rays and ultraviolet radiation constantly. While Earth's magnetic field and atmosphere prevent most space radiation from reaching the surface, a small amount penetrates. At the same time, ground radioactivity, from uranium in rocks, and especially from radon gas, constitutes a natural, terrestrial source of ionizing radiation, as do many foods, notably bananas. In higher altitudes, the natural radiation dose from space increases. People living in Denver, for instance, receive more radiation as compared with those living at sea level. Overall, a typical individual in the United States receives an annual approximate dose of 3 millisieverts (mSv), which is not harmful.

3. D: X-rays can have a variety of effects, depending on the intensity and duration of the exposure, the shape and direction of the x-ray beam, the anatomic area that is hit, and, probably, an individual's genetic makeup. While x-rays can damage cell structures and DNA, complex repair mechanisms have evolved. When functioning normally, cells can repair themselves, if the x-ray dose is modest. On the other hand, if a cell receives a very high dose, it may simply die in a process known as apoptosis. In between these two outcomes are numerous scenarios in which a cell may attempt to repair itself, but with errors. Exposure levels separating these outcomes are not known, but probably vary from person to person. Additionally, age is a factor. X-rays also may penetrate tissue with no interactions, while low-intensity, wide-beam x-rays may simply bounce off the skin.

4. A: Exposure to ionizing radiation may be quantified in terms of the dose that an individual receives during an acute event or in terms of cumulative exposure over a time period. Thus, doubling the time that one spends near a particular radiation source doubles the cumulative radiation dose. Exposure can be reduced by increasing the amount of shielding between the radiation source and the individual. It also can be reduced by increasing the individual's distance from the radiation source, the intensity of the radiation at a given location being inversely proportional to the square of the distance from the radiation source. The intensity of the radiation at the source, in turn, depends on the nature of the source and its energy. Thus, given the same shielding, distance, and exposure time, dosage is higher for an individual working with a high-energy source, such as a proton beam, than for an individual working with a weak radionuclide, such as tritium.

5. D: The intensity of ionizing radiation decreases with the distance from the radiation source according to the inverse square law. Thus, if the distance in this case were doubled, from 1 meter to 2, the radiation dosage received per time would decrease 4 times, which is to say from 2 to 0.5 μSv.

Since the distance in this case is tripled, however, the dosage decreases by 3 squared, or 9 times, resulting in a weekly exposure of 0.22 μSv. The first choice, 0.67 μSv is the result of simply dividing the original exposure by 3, without squaring, while 6 μSv would be an exposure increased 3 times.

6. B: Compared with most other medical imaging modalities, computed tomography (CT) scanning provides relatively high exposure to ionizing radiation, with 40 millisieverts (mSv) falling in the normal range for a full-body CT. Flat film chest x-ray radiography (lateral and posterior-anterior) imparts ionizing radiation doses typically in the range of 10 to 100 microsieverts (μSv), but the dose should not be as high as 1 mSv. Dental x-rays typically are in the area of 5 μSv, with some variation, but should not provide exposures as high as 50 μSv. For a passenger flying from New York to San Francisco, an exposure of approximately 40 μSv is typical because of increased exposure to cosmic radiation as one ascends to higher altitudes.

7. A: Radiation monitoring badges contain film that changes when it is exposed to ionizing radiation. Often, such badges are divided into different areas made of different materials to detect separately a worker's exposure to alpha particles, beta particles, and x-ray and gamma rays. After a certain time interval, often 1 month, the badge is sent to be developed in a laboratory to see how much of each type of radiation a worker has received. To present an accurate picture of one's radiation exposure, a badge must be worn at all times when the worker is in a radiation area, but kept away from radiation when not being worn. Since the neck to pelvis regions are the most critical anatomic areas to protect, this is where the badge should be worn. While a radiation badge detects radiation, it offers no protection to the person who wears it.

8. C: Because it has particular affinity for the thyroid gland, where it can concentrate and release gamma radiation that can destroy tissue and lead to thyroid malignancy, 125I is particularly hazardous when taken into the body. Moreover, since the molecular form of iodine (I2) is volatile, internal exposure to 125I can take place through inhalation, while certain 125I compounds can be absorbed through gloves. For these reasons, concern about gamma radiation from 125I is somewhat greater with respect to the possibility of internal, rather than external, exposure. Nevertheless, since a small bottle of 125I does indeed release a fair amount of gamma radiation, the possibility of external exposure should warrant a moderate level of concern.

9. D: X-rays and gamma rays are blocked best by materials made of atoms with large nuclei. For this reason, lead is the shield of choice in clinical settings where the sizes of radiation sources are fairly small and where walls and barriers around such equipment must be reasonably thin. Around large sources such as nuclear reactors, however, cement is used, often mixed with barium sulfate (barite or baryte), which also is radiation-dense, and with a thin layer of lead. Being a liquid, barium sulfate also is used as a contrast material in various radiographic applications that use x-rays to image internal structures. Depleted uranium is uranium whose ratio of 235U:238U has been reduced from that typical of uranium ore. Although it manifests its own radioactivity, depleted uranium actually makes an excellent shield against x and gamma radiation.

10. A: In contrast to the threshold model, which posits that exposure to ionizing radiation must not be harmful below a certain threshold, the linear no-threshold model (LNT) assumes that any ionizing radiation can be harmful, even the background radiation dose that all people receive naturally from the environment. The LNT model is called "linear," because a line is graphed for low-dose exposures by extrapolating backwards from a line calculated from high-dose data. These high-dose data come from populations known to have suffered harmful effects from fairly high radiation exposures. If even very small radiation exposures can increase an individual's risk of ill effects, it follows that damage resulting from low-level exposure is cumulative for any given individual. Since it is known that cells actually do repair, not only radiation-induced DNA breakage, but damage to other cell structures, the LNT model has been challenged. If the LNT is wrong, the effects of chronic, low-level radiation exposure should not be cumulative at all. Nevertheless, in health care settings, a policy of "as low as reasonably achievable" (ALARA) is followed.

11. D: Alpha radiation consists of alpha particles, each of which is made of two neutrons and two protons. Essentially, an alpha particle is a helium nucleus, except that it originates as a decay product of certain larger atoms. Being much more massive than beta particles (which are produced in a different radioactive decay process), alpha particles can be very destructive to tissue, but only if produced from within the body, as they have great difficulty penetrating through almost any material, including skin. Thus, not only lead, but windows, surgical scrubs, and even one sheet of paper, will stop alpha radiation.

12. B: 5 millisieverts (mSv) is the occupational dose limit for a pregnant worker, and thus for her embryo/fetus. This is the total, cumulative limit, applying to the entire gestational period, which usually is 40 weeks. Generally, supervisors prefer to keep their pregnant workers below this limit; when a worker's dose exceeds this limit (based on her radiation badge readings), she is not assigned duties that will increase her exposure still more. To appreciate how conservative this occupation exposure limit is, keep in mind that the average exposure to ionizing radiation from natural background sources for an individual living in the United States is 3 mSv per year, and up to 6 mSv per year in high altitude locations, such as Denver and Salt Lake City. If a radiation worker does not declare her pregnancy, her supervisor is not required to know about it, and thus has no obligation to change her duties.

13. C: In any electrical device that uses a vacuum tube, the cathode is the part from which electrons are emitted while the part to which the electrons flow is known as the anode. In an x-ray tube, the anode is made from a material such as molybdenum, copper, or especially tungsten. When a beam of electrons strikes such an anode, approximately 1 percent of the energy is converted to x-radiation through a phenomenon known as the Bremsstrahlung effect, and through another process known as K-shell emission. When this happens, the x-rays are emitted generally perpendicular to the path of the electrons. The rest of the energy is released as heat. Consisting of two protons and two neutrons, alpha particles are nucleons that are emitted from certain atoms during a radioactive decay process.

14. A: Diagnostic imaging requires x-radiation sufficient to penetrate body parts and ionize photographic materials to generate an image. In such cases, the most common application of x-rays in health care, x-ray tubes, are supplied an electric potential in the range of 30 to 150 kilovolts (kV, or kVp). While this range generates x-rays that are considered superficial for therapeutic applications (radiation therapy), some therapeutic applications make use of it. Many therapeutic applications, however, are in the megavoltage range, using devices such as betatrons and linear accelerators that operate above 1,000 kV. In between is a range known as orthovoltage therapy, generally defined as employing radiation produced from 120 to 1,000 kV.

15. D: Any imaging modality that creates images of something in slices or sections is a type of tomography. Thus, applications of tomography are used not only in medicine, but also in diverse areas, such as astrophysics, geophysics, oceanography, and archaeology. In positron emission tomography (PET), patients are given a substance that emits positrons and whose metabolism is relevant to the function of cells within tissue that needs to be imaged. Each positron released collides immediately with an electron, resulting in annihilation of the pair and the generation of gamma rays. These, in turn, are detected by a gamma camera and used in image production. In single-photon emission computed tomography (SPECT), patients are given gamma-emitting substances whose emissions are detected with gamma cameras, then used to create tomographic images. CT uses x-rays. The radio waves used in MRI, which also is a form of tomography, are a form of nonionizing radiation.

16. B: The quality of a radiographic image can be compromised by a variety of factors. While improper placement of a lead apron or other protective shield (such as a neck protector) can compromise the quality of an image by blocking what needs to be x-rayed, this would not make an image foggy or blurry. On the other hand, warped cassettes, dirt on the photographic material, and leakage of light into development chambers can indeed blur images. Thus, radiographers must conduct proper inspections of plates, cassettes, and rooms or chambers where image development takes place.

17. D: The energy of electromagnetic radiation, including x-rays, is given by the equation $E = hc/\lambda$, where E is the energy and λ is the wavelength. At the same time, energy (E) is proportional to voltage. Thus, v and λ are inversely proportional, which means that increasing the voltage shortens the wavelength of an x-ray beam. This, in turn, constitutes an increase in the beam's energy. The shorter the wavelength, the denser the tissue the x-rays can penetrate. Thus, as λ is shortened, the ability of x-radiation to distinguish between bone and soft tissue increases, since very long x-rays are absorbed even by soft tissue. However, if λ is shortened too much, bone itself becomes transparent, rendering the imaging technology useless. While changing the current through an x-ray tube does not alter the wavelength, it does affect the beam's intensity.

18. A: The intensity of an x-ray image depends on a function known as milliampere seconds (mAs), which is the product of the current and the time that the beam is turned on. Thus, if the current or the time is increased, the intensity is increased accordingly. However, if the current or the time is increased, decreasing the other will be counterproductive. Changing the voltage (kV or kVp) through the x-ray tube while keeping the current the same will not change the intensity of the image, but it will affect the ability to visualize various tissues.

19. C: Whether a radiography facility uses manual or automated processing of films, chemical checks of processing solutions are vital to ensure that images will be of high quality. In the case of automatic processors, testing the pH of developing and fixing solutions and replenishers should be performed daily. Other chemical tests of the solutions should include silver levels and specific gravity. The optimal values for all of these properties vary, depending on the type of developer and fixer used, and should be maintained according to the recommendations supplied by the manufacturer.

20. D: If a projection x-ray machine is being used constantly and producing images of consistent quality, its parts, such as the x-ray tube, must be inspected often. Since the interior glass becomes coated with tungsten, which can lead to instable function, the tube needs to be checked often because it may need to be replaced. If such checking is performed, and if regular radiation checks are taken for the room and of workers, the machine is taken to be working well. Thus, the Department of Health requires calibrations every 2 years, although annual calibration of equipment is prudent.

21. A: Development fog, also called "true fog," results from events in the development room or in automatic processing equipment, such as chemical contamination, high temperature of developing fluid, or too much time in the developing fluid. The average film density is related to how the film density changes as the amount of exposure changes. Specifically, it is the average slope between two chosen optical density values. For medical radiography, it ranges from 0.25 and 2. Film speed is an expression of how quickly a film develops. Since all three values vary based on the temperature of processing solutions, each is plotted against temperature in intervals of 1°C.

22. C: Radiography utilizing x-rays is extremely useful in the visualization of dense tissue, particularly bone. For this reason, simple, flat radiographs are used in the diagnosis of bone fractures, in which case the fracture appears as an area less radiodense than the rest of the bone. Since osteosarcoma tends to develop in long bones, simple, flat radiography often is all that is needed to identify it, prior to surgical biopsy (which allows for histopathologic characterization, which influences the treatment plan). Pneumonia is easily identified with simply, flat film radiography because the inflammatory effect in lung tissue increases the radiodensity. However, x-rays are not very effective in the imaging of soft tissue pathology, such a tear in the anterior cruciate ligament (ACL) of a knee.

23. A: With an estimated incidence of 5 percent of the United States population, obesity is a major problem, both from the perspective of public health and for clinical practice. In the case of radiology and radiography, a high amount of body fat adds technical complications to routine imaging. While most health care practitioners are well aware of the difficulty that obesity brings to imaging with ultrasonography, imaging modalities that use radiation are similarly compromised. This includes nuclear imaging, computed tomography, plain film radiography, and fluoroscopy. Magnetic resonance imaging is least affected by obesity, though it is subject to increased noise. While diabetes mellitus and atherosclerosis both are common, major health problems, each presents no particular issue with respect to the acquisition of radiographic images.

24. B: Contrast media, also called contrast agents, are helpful in the imaging of various anatomic structures and body fluids. There are two types of contrast media. Positive contrast media are radio-opaque, and increase the visibility of whatever they touch, or within whatever fluid they flow (blood, for instance). Negative contrast agents are less radio-opaque than the tissue that the touch, or through which they flow, and are dark on films. Contrast media do not protect patients against radiation, but often reduce the amount of radiation that is necessary to project in order to produce an image. Unlike radiotracers, which are used in nuclear imaging, contrast media are not radioactive.

25. D: When they were first discovered, and for many years after, x radiation and gamma radiation were distinguished in terms of their relative energy, with x being of longer wavelength, and thus lower frequency and energy, compared with gamma rays. The electromagnetic spectrum ran from x-rays into gamma rays, with the division defined at a certain point. In subsequent years, however, it was discovered that x-rays of very short wavelength could be produced, while gamma rays with wavelength longer than what normally were thought of as x-rays were found to be emitted by certain radioactive nuclei. Today, the distinction between these two forms of electromagnetic radiation is based on how each is produced, x-rays from electrons and gamma rays from atomic nuclei. Gamma rays also are produced in the process of annihilation, wherein two opposite particles, such as an electron and a positron, meet up, resulting in the annihilation of both and their mass converted to energy in the form of gamma radiation.

26. A: The energy of x-rays and all categories of electromagnetic radiation is given by the equation $E = hc/\lambda$, where E is the energy and λ is the wavelength. At the same time, energy (E) is proportional to voltage. Thus, v and λ are inversely proportional, which means that increasing the voltage shortens the wavelength of an x-ray beam. The value for λ, however, represents only the most energetic photons among all that are produced by the x-ray tube. Metals, such as aluminum, absorb the lower energy x-rays (those with a longer λ), while the higher energy x-rays pass through. Thus, sending the beam through filters sets a maximum on how long the waves reaching the patient can be. Filters are used because the lower energy x-rays are not useful in the generation of images but still can harm tissue, at least near the surface. Also, since the lower energy x-rays tend to scatter, if not filtered they would strike not only the target area on the patient, but other areas as well.

27. C: The half-value layer (HVL) represents the thickness of a material that is needed to absorb 50 percent of a beam's energy. Thus, it is given in units of distance, usually millimeters (mm) or centimeters (cm). The higher the energy (the shorter the wavelength) of an x-ray beam, the more easily it penetrates a given material, and the higher its HVL. The HVL is inversely proportional to the attenuation coefficient, but the former is what is used to express a beam's quality. Half-life is given in units of time and used to express how quickly, or how slowly, a radioactive substance decays, or how long any substance endures in the body before it is eliminated, or metabolized to something else. Radiographic density is an expression of the degree of darkening throughout a film.

28. C: Radiographic contrast is an expression of the differences (light vs dark) that are seen between various tissues imaged during radiography. Scattered x-ray photons can increase the overall exposure, reducing the contrast. Thus, contrast can be improved by reducing the amount of scattering. Higher voltage creates x-rays of shorter wavelength, which penetrate tissue better than longer waves; increasing the voltage, not decreasing it, can improve contrast. Decreasing the current reduces the intensity of the beam, reducing the overall exposure of the film, without changing the contrast. Decreasing the amount of time that the beam is on also reduces the overall film exposure without changing the contrast.

29. B: Radiographic density of a tissue (how radio-opaque the tissue appears in radiography) depends on how well it can stop x-ray photons, absorbing their energy in the process. This is determined by the number of electrons contained within a given volume of tissue, since electrons are what absorb the energy. Bone does contain more water than fat does, but this is not why bone stops more x-rays. Bone consists largely of calcium and phosphorus, which are fairly large atoms and contain many electrons. Fat tissue, on the other hand, contains mostly molecules built of carbon backbones, so the concentration of electrons is slightly less than that of soft tissue, such as cartilage, and a lot less than that of bone. Nevertheless, fat is still more radio-opaque than air, or other gases. Thus, obese patients produce radiographs of reduced quality.

30. A: Fat is more radiolucent than both bone and soft tissue, but still stops x-rays much better than air. Thus, obese individuals are indeed more difficult to image because the x-rays must penetrate thick layers of fat to reach internal structures. While this might suggest that the thinner the patient is the better, people with extremely low body fat can lose the fat around internal organs. Not only does this fat play a protective role, but in radiography it serves as contrast material to elucidate the exact shape of the organs as well as other internal structures. Thus, while bone tissue shows up as being very light, fat appears as a shade of gray, making the internal organs stand out against the black background.

31. D: A radiograph taken in the PA or AP orientations should make it possible to view the entire thoracic cavity. The costophrenic angle, lateral and medial lung fields, and bases of each lung are included in this region. Silhouettes of the heart and trachea should be visible superimposed on the upper thoracic vertebrae. At least 10 posterior ribs, not merely 8, should be visible. Through the mediastinum, the lower thoracic vertebral bodies should be visible as well. In order to bring all of these areas within the image, the patient must be positioned correctly and should have inspired and be holding his or her breath when the image is taken, which increases the size of the thoracic cavity.

32. B: Overpenetration means that the ability of the x-ray beam to penetrate materials is so good that much of the energy passes through all body tissues, including bone. This makes bone tissue more lucent than it should be so that it appears like the way that soft tissue is supposed to appear. Soft tissue, as well as fat, appears still more lucent such that they may not even be visible. Increased penetration of a beam is the result of increased voltage, not decreased. As the voltage is increased, the energy of the x-rays increases, which is to say that the wavelength (λ) is shortened, improving the beam's quality. There comes a point, however, when λ is so short that the penetration is too good, decreasing the visibility of everything. While the electrical current (mAs) affects the intensity of the beam (the number of x-ray photons emitted) and can affect the contrast, it does not affect the ability of the photons to penetrate materials.

33. C: Flat film chest radiography is taken in either a PA or AP orientation, and also may be taken in a lateral orientation. PA means that the patient is with his or her back toward the machine, so that the x-rays enter through the back and exit through the chest on their way to the photographic plate. AP is the opposite, so the patient is with the chest toward the machine. Lateral means that the beam passes from one side of the rib cage to the other. For chest x-radiography, it is better if the patient stands, in which case PA is usually the orientation used. When a patient is too ill to be moved, a portable machine is brought to the bedside. Usually it is easier for the patient to be supine, rather than prone, so the orientation is AP.

34. A: When compared with the PA view, the heart and mediastinum appear magnified when the AP orientation is used. This is because these structures are slightly further away from the photographic plate when the beam enters the chest and exits through the back than in the opposite scenario. To visualize why this is the case, think of a flashlight shining on your hand to project a shadow on the wall. Move the hand back from the wall and the image gets larger. Enlargement of either the heart or mediastinum can have very important clinical implications. This is one reason why it is important not to mislabel an AP image as a PA image, or vice versa.

35. B: The resistance of a radiograph to color change is known as its archival quality and is related mostly to the residual level of ammonium thiosulfate. With ammonium thiosulfate levels above 25 µgm/in2, radiographs tend to turn yellow within a year, but they tend not to turn brown unless ammonium thiosulfate levels are above 100 µgm/in2. Low density overall on a film can be the result of the film not being in the developing fluid long enough, a lower than optimal temperature of the developing fluid, or exhausted developing material. Graying with a loss of contrast could be the result of a film being underdeveloped or overexposed.

36. D: Developing solution on hangar clips can drip down along the film when it is supposed to be drying after being rinsed of developing solution. Drops falling down along the film in this situation create streaks that overdevelop in relation to the rest of the film. However, if developing solution is on the film prior to processing, this tends to produce spots rather than streaks, generally dark spots. Fixer on the film prior to processing will produce white spots, since the film reacts to the fixer as if x-rays did not reach it because of blockage by radio-opaque tissue. Temperature differences between solutions cause shrinking and swelling of the film, which produces reticular patterns.

37. D: The only difference between the upper and lower parts of the film is that the latter was lower in the tank compared with the former. Since the developing agent is dissolved, it is present throughout the tank at the same concentration. However, it is very easy for temperature differences to develop within the tank, if the solution is not stirred on a regular basis. Since the film was in the tank when the unequal development took place, fixer would not be the problem, unless someone entered the room, removed the film from the development tank, dipped the lower end into the fixer tank, and then placed it back into the developer. Such an occurrence is even less likely if the film is handled by automatic processing equipment. A light leak would affect the entire film, as would early or late removal of the film from the developer, due to a malfunctioning timer.

38. B: Digital radiography refers to imaging that is processed directly as computer images, without the use of films and the developing and fixing agents that go with them. It is akin to digital photography, in which files are digital and printed as hard copies only if needed. Since many of the common errors in radiography occur during the processing of film (eg, developing, rinsing, fixing) after the patient been in the machine, increased use of digital radiography would reduce the number of errors that lead to the need for repeat radiographs. Without the film processing, images are available for diagnostic purposes much sooner, compared with analogue radiography, and images are saved digitally, rather than as films.

39. A: Fog is what results from the development of film grains that are unexposed to radiation, or exposed accidentally. If due to accidental exposure of grains, the fog is called exposure fog. Development fog, also called "true fog," results from events in the development room or in automatic processing equipment, such as chemical contamination, high temperature of developing fluid, or too much time in the developing fluid. While mottle also appears grainy, it is caused by defects in x-ray intensifying screens, or by quantum effects. Radiographic noise can have many causes, but appears when film is developed. Thus, undeveloped film cannot be used to measure it.

40. C: Overdevelopment of radiographic film occurs when the chemical reaction that changes the appearance of the film grains is accelerated, or goes on for too long. Removing the film too early would lead to underdevelopment of a film. Since the chemical reaction that underlies the development speeds up with increasing temperature, lowering the temperature also would lead to an underdeveloped film. Contamination of the developer would reduce its efficiency, also leading to underdevelopment. However, not mixing the developer correctly could lead either to overdevelopment or underdevelopment, depending on what the mixing error is. If the solution were too concentrated, overdevelopment would be expected.

41. D: Grit on a radiographic film is the result of dirt in the washing water, in one of the solutions, or anywhere in an automatic processor. In such cases, the solutions should be changed and the equipment cleaned. If developing solution is on the film prior to processing, this tends to produce dark spots on the film. Fixer on the film prior to processing will produce white spots, since the film reacts to the fixer, as if x-rays did not reach it because of blockage by radio-opaque tissue. Temperature differences between solutions cause shrinking and swelling of the film, which produces reticular patterns.

42. C: Imaging with CT scanning often is performed both with and without a contrast medium. Such media are given to patients to increase the radio-opacity of soft tissue structures such as the gastrointestinal tract, or blood vessels. Also known as contrast agents, contrast media also are used with flat film radiography and with fluoroscopy. Barium is used is procedures such as a barium swallow to enhance visibility of the upper gastrointestinal tract (esophagus, stomach, duodenum), while a barium enema enhances the visibility of lower gastrointestinal structures, such as the sigmoid colon. Once the target structures are coated with barium, standard flat radiography is used. Most of the CT procedures with contrast use iodine-based agents. Like iodine, bromine and fluorine are halogens, which could lead to confusion if one does not read the answer choices carefully. An isotope of fluorine (18F) is used often as a positron source in PET, which could confuse the test taker.

43. A: MRI is considered to be one of the best imaging modalities because it is particularly good at elucidating soft tissue. This is because MRI works based on the quantum properties of protons, which is to say hydrogen nuclei. Hydrogen is abundant in soft tissues, including loose connective, muscle, and nervous tissue, which are more difficult to see in detail with imaging modalities that use x-rays. Very subtle differences between the hydrogen milieu of these tissues allows for excellent visualization. Unlike CT scanning, MRI does not expose patients to ionizing radiation, but this is not a reason why it is particularly good for the imaging of various soft tissues and to detect and visualize neoplasia. These advantages notwithstanding, MRI is fairly complex and expensive. Moreover, since it makes use of a very powerful magnetic field, it can be dangerous for people with metal implants, or other metal in their bodies. In the case of a cardiac pacemaker, or an aneurism clip in the brain, exposure to such a strong magnetic field could be immediately fatal. On the other hand, certain new cochlear implants have been approved for MRI, as are implants made of titanium (or its alloys), which is not magnetic and will not move when the magnetic field is activated.

44. B: The Towne method is a type of anteroposterior position wherein the central ray (CR) of an x-ray beam is aimed at the cranium just above the glabella (the part between the eyebrows) at a 30-degree angle toward the patient's feet. The Caldwell method is a PA orientation in which the beam enters from the back, through the occipital region. In the lateral position for skull radiography, the CR enters just above the external auditory meatus. The Towne method is used to image the occipital bone, foramen magnum, and dorsum sellae.

45. D: For a radiograph with a view of the shoulder joint in internal rotation, the patient is instructed to place the dorsal (posterior) aspect of the hand against the thigh. By doing this, the patient will have supinated the forearm. Often, to ensure that the correct position is achieved, the radiographer needs to position the arm for the patient, and then explain that it should be maintained in this position until the x-ray is taken. If the patient has sustained a shoulder injury, holding the position may be difficult, so devices may be needed to support the arm.

46. B: The positioning described in the question is known as the Kuchendorf method, which is used for providing oblique PA projection of a knee. The Judet view involves raising both legs at a 45-degree angle to provide an oblique projection of the acetabulum. The Johnson method is for imaging the femoral neck and head, with the photographic plate positioned laterally against the hip that needs to be imaged. The Lilienfeld position is used to image the acetabulum and ileum from a posterolateral orientation. The central ray is at the level of the greater trochanter, which is touching the photographic plate, with the patient prone and the opposite leg raised 75 degrees, to keep it out of the way.

47. C: Although severe reactions to contrast media are rare, the possibility needs to be taken seriously. Sensitivity to iodine is usually the reason for the reaction. Thus, if a patient has a sensation of swelling or notes pain, the injection should be stopped. For a power injection, a plastic cannula is preferred, since it is flexible. Both power injection and bolus injection are better than drip infusion. Laws regarding who may administer contrast media vary by state, so it is important to know the rules of the municipality where the hospital or imaging facility is located. Often, licensed radiographic technicians and nurses are permitted to administer contrast media. In some cases, a radiologist is required to be present, but this is not the case in all states.

48. D: Often patients are inundated with a great deal of misinformation from various sources. As an experienced radiographic technician, you should have a very good idea of the relative exposures to ionizing radiation from different sources. In this case, the radiologist would know the same as you: that the potential exposure that the fetus could receive is extremely low. This is because of the shielding that you will place around the patient's torso, and also because even the radiation aimed at the wrist will be of a low dose, on the order of a few microsieverts (μSv). In contrast, on the typical flight from Europe to North America, the patient, wearing no shielding, probably received a dose in the area of 100 μSv, depending on the altitude of the flight, how far north it was, and the amount of solar flare activity. After explaining this, make sure that you also explain that the dose that the patient received on the flight also is small, about 1/30th of the average person's annual radiation exposure from natural sources. This should provide the patient with a realistic perspective. If she still is not satisfied, calling in the radiologist to reiterate what you have said would be appropriate. Telling the patient that you have never seen any problems in all of your years might strike her as condescending, while questioning the physician's order for the film is not appropriate.

49. A: As tempting as it may be, it is not appropriate for a radiographic technician to reveal what he or she has seen, no matter how simple and obvious the diagnosis appears to be. The ARRT ethical code sets a clear boundary between the duties of the radiography technologist and the physician, whether a radiologist, emergency department physician, orthopedic surgeon, or other physician is to make the diagnosis. As your experience grows, you will see the most common diagnoses many times. In many cases, you will know the diagnosis before the film is read by a physician. Only rarely might you be confronted in this way by a patient or a parent, but in such cases, it is important to remind them of your role.

50. C: Dental fillings almost always are made of materials that are not affected by magnetic fields. Certain other dental work, however, could be slightly affected, generally not enough to cause danger, but could distort images, and should be reported to the radiologist. Jewelry and body piercings certainly must be removed. The magnetic field is so powerful that such objects can move with significant force. For the same reason, MRI is contraindicated in patients with metal implants, such as aneurism clips or cardiac pacemakers, because the results of exposure to such a strong magnetic field can be fatal. Generally, such implants are not missed when charts and patient histories are assessed during workups prior to ordering an MRI, but they must be included on MRI screening forms. If brought near the MRI magnet, credit cards and other devices with magnetic strips will be erased, so warn patients not to bring wallets or purses into the MRI scanning room. Generally, radiologists, radiographic technicians, and others who work around the equipment are the ones whose credit cards get erased, as they forget to leave them aside when running into the scanning room in haste. Cell phones and other electronic devices also can be harmed.

How to Overcome Test Anxiety

Just the thought of taking a test is enough to make most people a little nervous. A test is an important event that can have a long-term impact on your future, so it's important to take it seriously and it's natural to feel anxious about performing well. But just because anxiety is normal, that doesn't mean that it's helpful in test taking, or that you should simply accept it as part of your life. Anxiety can have a variety of effects. These effects can be mild, like making you feel slightly nervous, or severe, like blocking your ability to focus or remember even a simple detail.

If you experience test anxiety—whether severe or mild—it's important to know how to beat it. To discover this, first you need to understand what causes test anxiety.

Causes of Test Anxiety

While we often think of anxiety as an uncontrollable emotional state, it can actually be caused by simple, practical things. One of the most common causes of test anxiety is that a person does not feel adequately prepared for their test. This feeling can be the result of many different issues such as poor study habits or lack of organization, but the most common culprit is time management. Starting to study too late, failing to organize your study time to cover all of the material, or being distracted while you study will mean that you're not well prepared for the test. This may lead to cramming the night before, which will cause you to be physically and mentally exhausted for the test. Poor time management also contributes to feelings of stress, fear, and hopelessness as you realize you are not well prepared but don't know what to do about it.

Other times, test anxiety is not related to your preparation for the test but comes from unresolved fear. This may be a past failure on a test, or poor performance on tests in general. It may come from comparing yourself to others who seem to be performing better or from the stress of living up to expectations. Anxiety may be driven by fears of the future—how failure on this test would affect your educational and career goals. These fears are often completely irrational, but they can still negatively impact your test performance.

Elements of Test Anxiety

As mentioned earlier, test anxiety is considered to be an emotional state, but it has physical and mental components as well. Sometimes you may not even realize that you are suffering from test anxiety until you notice the physical symptoms. These can include trembling hands, rapid heartbeat, sweating, nausea, and tense muscles. Extreme anxiety may lead to fainting or vomiting. Obviously, any of these symptoms can have a negative impact on testing. It is important to recognize them as soon as they begin to occur so that you can address the problem before it damages your performance.

The mental components of test anxiety include trouble focusing and inability to remember learned information. During a test, your mind is on high alert, which can help you recall information and stay focused for an extended period of time. However, anxiety interferes with your mind's natural processes, causing you to blank out, even on the questions you know well. The strain of testing during anxiety makes it difficult to stay focused, especially on a test that may take several hours. Extreme anxiety can take a huge mental toll, making it difficult not only to recall test information but even to understand the test questions or pull your thoughts together.

Effects of Test Anxiety

Test anxiety is like a disease—if left untreated, it will get progressively worse. Anxiety leads to poor performance, and this reinforces the feelings of fear and failure, which in turn lead to poor performances on subsequent tests. It can grow from a mild nervousness to a crippling condition. If allowed to progress, test anxiety can have a big impact on your schooling, and consequently on your future.

Test anxiety can spread to other parts of your life. Anxiety on tests can become anxiety in any stressful situation, and blanking on a test can turn into panicking in a job situation. But fortunately, you don't have to let anxiety rule your testing and determine your grades. There are a number of relatively simple steps you can take to move past anxiety and function normally on a test and in the rest of life.

Physical Steps for Beating Test Anxiety

While test anxiety is a serious problem, the good news is that it can be overcome. It doesn't have to control your ability to think and remember information. While it may take time, you can begin taking steps today to beat anxiety.

Just as your first hint that you may be struggling with anxiety comes from the physical symptoms, the first step to treating it is also physical. Rest is crucial for having a clear, strong mind. If you are tired, it is much easier to give in to anxiety. But if you establish good sleep habits, your body and mind will be ready to perform optimally, without the strain of exhaustion. Additionally, sleeping well helps you to retain information better, so you're more likely to recall the answers when you see the test questions.

Getting good sleep means more than going to bed on time. It's important to allow your brain time to relax. Take study breaks from time to time so it doesn't get overworked, and don't study right before bed. Take time to rest your mind before trying to rest your body, or you may find it difficult to fall asleep.

Along with sleep, other aspects of physical health are important in preparing for a test. Good nutrition is vital for good brain function. Sugary foods and drinks may give a burst of energy but this burst is followed by a crash, both physically and emotionally. Instead, fuel your body with protein and vitamin-rich foods.

Also, drink plenty of water. Dehydration can lead to headaches and exhaustion, especially if your brain is already under stress from the rigors of the test. Particularly if your test is a long one, drink water during the breaks. And if possible, take an energy-boosting snack to eat between sections.

Along with sleep and diet, a third important part of physical health is exercise. Maintaining a steady workout schedule is helpful, but even taking 5-minute study breaks to walk can help get your blood pumping faster and clear your head. Exercise also releases endorphins, which contribute to a positive feeling and can help combat test anxiety.

When you nurture your physical health, you are also contributing to your mental health. If your body is healthy, your mind is much more likely to be healthy as well. So take time to rest, nourish your body with healthy food and water, and get moving as much as possible. Taking these physical steps will make you stronger and more able to take the mental steps necessary to overcome test anxiety.

Mental Steps for Beating Test Anxiety

Working on the mental side of test anxiety can be more challenging, but as with the physical side, there are clear steps you can take to overcome it. As mentioned earlier, test anxiety often stems from lack of preparation, so the obvious solution is to prepare for the test. Effective studying may be the most important weapon you have for beating test anxiety, but you can and should employ several other mental tools to combat fear.

First, boost your confidence by reminding yourself of past success—tests or projects that you aced. If you're putting as much effort into preparing for this test as you did for those, there's no reason you should expect to fail here. Work hard to prepare; then trust your preparation.

Second, surround yourself with encouraging people. It can be helpful to find a study group, but be sure that the people you're around will encourage a positive attitude. If you spend time with others who are anxious or cynical, this will only contribute to your own anxiety. Look for others who are motivated to study hard from a desire to succeed, not from a fear of failure.

Third, reward yourself. A test is physically and mentally tiring, even without anxiety, and it can be helpful to have something to look forward to. Plan an activity following the test, regardless of the outcome, such as going to a movie or getting ice cream.

When you are taking the test, if you find yourself beginning to feel anxious, remind yourself that you know the material. Visualize successfully completing the test. Then take a few deep, relaxing breaths and return to it. Work through the questions carefully but with confidence, knowing that you are capable of succeeding.

Developing a healthy mental approach to test taking will also aid in other areas of life. Test anxiety affects more than just the actual test—it can be damaging to your mental health and even contribute to depression. It's important to beat test anxiety before it becomes a problem for more than testing.

Study Strategy

Being prepared for the test is necessary to combat anxiety, but what does being prepared look like? You may study for hours on end and still not feel prepared. What you need is a strategy for test prep. The next few pages outline our recommended steps to help you plan out and conquer the challenge of preparation.

Step 1: Scope Out the Test

Learn everything you can about the format (multiple choice, essay, etc.) and what will be on the test. Gather any study materials, course outlines, or sample exams that may be available. Not only will this help you to prepare, but knowing what to expect can help to alleviate test anxiety.

Step 2: Map Out the Material

Look through the textbook or study guide and make note of how many chapters or sections it has. Then divide these over the time you have. For example, if a book has 15 chapters and you have five days to study, you need to cover three chapters each day. Even better, if you have the time, leave an extra day at the end for overall review after you have gone through the material in depth.

If time is limited, you may need to prioritize the material. Look through it and make note of which sections you think you already have a good grasp on, and which need review. While you are studying, skim quickly through the familiar sections and take more time on the challenging parts.

Write out your plan so you don't get lost as you go. Having a written plan also helps you feel more in control of the study, so anxiety is less likely to arise from feeling overwhelmed at the amount to cover.

Step 3: Gather Your Tools

Decide what study method works best for you. Do you prefer to highlight in the book as you study and then go back over the highlighted portions? Or do you type out notes of the important information? Or is it helpful to make flashcards that you can carry with you? Assemble the pens, index cards, highlighters, post-it notes, and any other materials you may need so you won't be distracted by getting up to find things while you study.

If you're having a hard time retaining the information or organizing your notes, experiment with different methods. For example, try color-coding by subject with colored pens, highlighters, or post-it notes. If you learn better by hearing, try recording yourself reading your notes so you can listen while in the car, working out, or simply sitting at your desk. Ask a friend to quiz you from your flashcards, or try teaching someone the material to solidify it in your mind.

Step 4: Create Your Environment

It's important to avoid distractions while you study. This includes both the obvious distractions like visitors and the subtle distractions like an uncomfortable chair (or a too-comfortable couch that makes you want to fall asleep). Set up the best study environment possible: good lighting and a comfortable work area. If background music helps you focus, you may want to turn it on, but otherwise keep the room quiet. If you are using a computer to take notes, be sure you don't have any other windows open, especially applications like social media, games, or anything else that could distract you. Silence your phone and turn off notifications. Be sure to keep water close by so you stay hydrated while you study (but avoid unhealthy drinks and snacks).

Also, take into account the best time of day to study. Are you freshest first thing in the morning? Try to set aside some time then to work through the material. Is your mind clearer in the afternoon or evening? Schedule your study session then. Another method is to study at the same time of day that you will take the test, so that your brain gets used to working on the material at that time and will be ready to focus at test time.

Step 5: Study!

Once you have done all the study preparation, it's time to settle into the actual studying. Sit down, take a few moments to settle your mind so you can focus, and begin to follow your study plan. Don't give in to distractions or let yourself procrastinate. This is your time to prepare so you'll be ready to fearlessly approach the test. Make the most of the time and stay focused.

Of course, you don't want to burn out. If you study too long you may find that you're not retaining the information very well. Take regular study breaks. For example, taking five minutes out of every hour to walk briskly, breathing deeply and swinging your arms, can help your mind stay fresh.

As you get to the end of each chapter or section, it's a good idea to do a quick review. Remind yourself of what you learned and work on any difficult parts. When you feel that you've mastered the material, move on to the next part. At the end of your study session, briefly skim through your notes again.

But while review is helpful, cramming last minute is NOT. If at all possible, work ahead so that you won't need to fit all your study into the last day. Cramming overloads your brain with more information than it can process and retain, and your tired mind may struggle to recall even previously learned information when it is overwhelmed with last-minute study. Also, the urgent nature of cramming and the stress placed on your brain contribute to anxiety. You'll be more likely to go to the test feeling unprepared and having trouble thinking clearly.

So don't cram, and don't stay up late before the test, even just to review your notes at a leisurely pace. Your brain needs rest more than it needs to go over the information again. In fact, plan to finish your studies by noon or early afternoon the day before the test. Give your brain the rest of the day to relax or focus on other things, and get a good night's sleep. Then you will be fresh for the test and better able to recall what you've studied.

Step 6: Take a Practice Test

Many courses offer sample tests, either online or in the study materials. This is an excellent resource to check whether you have mastered the material, as well as to prepare for the test format and environment.

Check the test format ahead of time: the number of questions, the type (multiple choice, free response, etc.), and the time limit. Then create a plan for working through them. For example, if you have 30 minutes to take a 60-question test, your limit is 30 seconds per question. Spend less time on the questions you know well so that you can take more time on the difficult ones.

If you have time to take several practice tests, take the first one open book, with no time limit. Work through the questions at your own pace and make sure you fully understand them. Gradually work up to taking a test under test conditions: sit at a desk with all study materials put away and set a timer. Pace yourself to make sure you finish the test with time to spare and go back to check your answers if you have time.

After each test, check your answers. On the questions you missed, be sure you understand why you missed them. Did you misread the question (tests can use tricky wording)? Did you forget the information? Or was it something you hadn't learned? Go back and study any shaky areas that the practice tests reveal.

Taking these tests not only helps with your grade, but also aids in combating test anxiety. If you're already used to the test conditions, you're less likely to worry about it, and working through tests until you're scoring well gives you a confidence boost. Go through the practice tests until you feel comfortable, and then you can go into the test knowing that you're ready for it.

Test Tips

On test day, you should be confident, knowing that you've prepared well and are ready to answer the questions. But aside from preparation, there are several test day strategies you can employ to maximize your performance.

First, as stated before, get a good night's sleep the night before the test (and for several nights before that, if possible). Go into the test with a fresh, alert mind rather than staying up late to study.

Try not to change too much about your normal routine on the day of the test. It's important to eat a nutritious breakfast, but if you normally don't eat breakfast at all, consider eating just a protein bar. If you're a coffee drinker, go ahead and have your normal coffee. Just make sure you time it so that the caffeine doesn't wear off right in the middle of your test. Avoid sugary beverages, and drink enough water to stay hydrated but not so much that you need a restroom break 10 minutes into the test. If your test isn't first thing in the morning, consider going for a walk or doing a light workout before the test to get your blood flowing.

Allow yourself enough time to get ready, and leave for the test with plenty of time to spare so you won't have the anxiety of scrambling to arrive in time. Another reason to be early is to select a good seat. It's helpful to sit away from doors and windows, which can be distracting. Find a good seat, get out your supplies, and settle your mind before the test begins.

When the test begins, start by going over the instructions carefully, even if you already know what to expect. Make sure you avoid any careless mistakes by following the directions.

Then begin working through the questions, pacing yourself as you've practiced. If you're not sure on an answer, don't spend too much time on it, and don't let it shake your confidence. Either skip it and come back later, or eliminate as many wrong answers as possible and guess among the remaining ones. Don't dwell on these questions as you continue—put them out of your mind and focus on what lies ahead.

Be sure to read all of the answer choices, even if you're sure the first one is the right answer. Sometimes you'll find a better one if you keep reading. But don't second-guess yourself if you do immediately know the answer. Your gut instinct is usually right. Don't let test anxiety rob you of the information you know.

If you have time at the end of the test (and if the test format allows), go back and review your answers. Be cautious about changing any, since your first instinct tends to be correct, but make sure you didn't misread any of the questions or accidentally mark the wrong answer choice. Look over any you skipped and make an educated guess.

At the end, leave the test feeling confident. You've done your best, so don't waste time worrying about your performance or wishing you could change anything. Instead, celebrate the successful completion of this test. And finally, use this test to learn how to deal with anxiety even better next time.

Review Video: Test Anxiety
Visit mometrix.com/academy and enter code: 100340

Important Qualification

Not all anxiety is created equal. If your test anxiety is causing major issues in your life beyond the classroom or testing center, or if you are experiencing troubling physical symptoms related to your anxiety, it may be a sign of a serious physiological or psychological condition. If this sounds like your situation, we strongly encourage you to seek professional help.

Additional Bonus Material

Due to our efforts to try to keep this book to a manageable length, we've created a link that will give you access to all of your additional bonus material:

mometrix.com/bonus948/radiography

Made in the USA
Monee, IL
27 August 2024

64636588R00096